MANAGING TO CARE

in

Homes for the Elderly

James R Whitton

Head, Faculty of Community Studies,
Halton College, Widnes

PATTEN PRESS, NEWMILL
1995

First published in 1982. Patten Papers on Health Care 1.

Second edition, 1987

Third edition (revised), 1995

The Patten Press, The Old Post Office, Newmill, Penzance, Cornwall TR20 8 XN. Tel/fax 01736 330704.

ISBN 1 872229 18 2

Printed and bound in Great Britain by Cromwell Press, Broughton Gifford, Melksham, Wiltshire

CONTENTS

Preface to the Third Edition

Since *Managing to Care* was first written there has been significant change in the provision of residential care for the elderly. Social Service Departments have considerably reduced the number of their homes to become, in the main, purchasers of provision from the private and voluntary sectors, rather than suppliers of care themselves. As a result of this, and an increase in the elderly population as a whole, the private and voluntary sector has grown enormously. Nonetheless, the balance may swing either way, as the 'politics and finance of care' change and evolve.

With the ageing of the population as a whole, has come competition between the various providers, be they voluntary organisations, single owner/managers, large organisations or the surviving SSD homes themselves. Market forces now affect the provision of residential care to an extent that could not have been envisaged a few years ago. Homes are formally inspected and the reports made public. These reports are available to individuals contemplating residential care for themselves or their relatives and to the placement officers of SSDs who must assure themselves of the quality of care the homes provide. Quality assurance is at last penetrating residential care and will become the key to commercial success, if not survival.

This third edition has tried to take these important changes into account in its guidance to managers of residential homes.

In the text the feminine pronouns used to describe the Manager and her employees have been retained, even though the author is aware that many managers and some staff are male. This has been done to avoid repeated use of the cumbersome him/her, she/he expressions, and yet to keep the text as personal as possible..

Introduction

Occupants of residential homes for the elderly do not represent a cross-section of the elderly population: more than half are well over the age of 80 years old and, when compared with old people leading independent lives outside, they are handicapped by varying degrees of physical infirmity or mental confusion. It is precisely these handicaps that have necessitated their admittance to care at a stage in their lives when they are most vulnerable and least able to adjust to a new pattern of existence. The quality of care they receive from the staff will therefore determine to a great extent their future happiness and well being.

When elderly people find it impossible to continue life in a normal community and are forced to enter a Residential Home, there is no justification for assuming they suddenly become incapable of all independent actions. They will still wish to preserve their independence and privacy and maintain for themselves a place in the world. For prior to their admission they will have been accustomed to making decisions and acting upon them, and, providing they do not infringe the freedom of others, there is no reason why they should not continue doing so in the Home. In fact, wherever they are capable of managing their own affairs they should be actively encouraged to do so.

Those who look after the elderly have to steer a course between over-protection on the one hand and lack of necessary care on the other; providing sufficient support to give reassurance, yet urging residents to attempt individual action when they may be ready to give up. To make this all the more difficult, no two residents are alike in their infirmity, each having characteristic limitations demanding individual attention, placing considerable demands on the staff.

Although a desire to work with people rather than things is a starting point for a career in residential homes, other aptitudes, skills and knowledge are required. This is important in care staff who are in close daily contact with residents, but *vital* in the senior staff. The capacity to understand and manage people is one essential component in the armoury of Homes' Managers who need a whole battery of skills to run a Home for the Elderly. Their task is to analyse the needs of the residents, formulate objectives, organise the work of the staff and then motivate each worker to meet the objectives.

i

Management of people is a personal skill that some individuals possess naturally; others develop through trial and error; and some never bother to acquire adequately at all. When the quality of life of thousands of elderly people depends upon the managerial ability of Heads of Homes it is incumbent upon such key staff to become proficient in this skill.

This book is written in the hope that it will encourage senior staff and those who aspire to such appointments, to acquaint themselves with fundamental management principles. To make the reading both palatable and relevant, practical suggestions for putting these principles into action have been included. Principles and practice are working partners.

Much of what is written will appear elementary to readers who have studied management practice, but for those residential staff who have not touched upon the subject before, I hope the book provokes thought, stimulates further reading and tempts them to experiment with new approaches. 'Principled action' is the key.

James R Whitton, 1995

CHAPTER 1
The Residential Home & Its Purposes

The aim of a Residential Home for the elderly is to create a sheltered, caring environment for a group of men and women brought together by nothing other than the hazards of circumstance. In this Home, despite individual limitations, they may live out their lives in comfort, with dignity and purpose. It is the responsibility of the Manager of the Home to meet this aim by fully exploiting all resources, whether they are available in the Home, the community outside or in the related professions.

In essence, this is the stated purpose of a Residential Home for the elderly and the function of its most senior member of staff. In practice, however, the position is nowhere so clear or precise, as varied factors collectively conspire either to obscure the aim or effectively frustrate attempts to achieve it.

At work the Home's Manager has to contend with many competing demands on her limited time, energy and finances. Furthermore she may also be restricted by the physical resources of the building, since many Homes are in adapted premises. Add to this the conflicting opinions of private owners with their commercial pressures, or social service departments with politico-union constraints; relatives with their guilt complexes; staff with their own agendas at work; residents with their ideas -- or lack of them; and the size of the challenge facing the Manager becomes obvious.

Faced, therefore, with the pressures of reality the Home Manager has to choose between maintaining a running battle with the forces arrayed against her or accept modifications of her aim in order to placate some of the opposition. In these circumstances compromise appears to offer an attractive alternative for the harassed Manager and, in consequence, many homes fail to provide for their residents the degree of independence, dignity and purpose desired.

The Manager in a Residential Home has a complex role calling for a thorough understanding of the needs of the frail elderly, a desire and a will to serve their interests, and the skills necessary to manage staff and other resources in an effective way.

1.1 Competing influences

It is not an unusual for an observant, critical visitor in a Residential Home to leave with a feeling that the physical needs of the residents are well catered for but that social and emotional needs are being sadly neglected. The residents appear relatively inactive between mealtimes, seldom conversing with each other and displaying symptoms characteristic of the institutionalised mind. The observant visitor will attribute these signs to a lack of stimulation and opportunity for activity rather than to the absence in the residents of the necessary human and physical resources to be otherwise.

The honest, competent Manager will already have made the same observation herself, though being in regular contact with the residents she may have convinced herself of many reasons for their lethargy that seemingly exonerate her from blame. She is likely to have made a mental list of all those factors that militate against the provision in her Home of an environment that is sufficiently stimulating to ward off institutional neurosis. Some of these factors are listed here, together with others of which she may not be conscious.

A. The residents themselves, having in their earlier days been introduced to the Home's routine by established occupants, may refuse to take part in simple domestic activities, such as laying tables, clearing pots or peeling vegetables, in the belief that it is the staff's responsibility to attend to all domestic duties. These residents in turn influence newcomers into accepting the same philosophy. Resistance to change is therefore high, and the staff face an uphill struggle in attempting to persuade the residents to involve themselves in the simple functions that would not only relieve the monotony of their daily routine but, in themselves, be therapeutic activities for hands and limbs.

B. Such an attitude may be encouraged by anxious relatives and harassed placement officers who, when confronted with opposition to residential accommodation from elderly clients, lay great stress on how the Homes' staff will be on call all day, how meals will be provided, baths run, beds made and rooms cleaned...all of these without a mention that residential accommodation will involve a degree of self-care. Thus, new residents arrive at the Home already anticipating service akin to hotel care, making them easy prey for existing residents who are only too anxious to explain, in concise terms, how they see the duties of the care staff.

C. Those residents who have not been cajoled into residential care by such persuasions, but who have entered under their own volition, bring with them the same expectations -- and possibly more -- simply because they are paying the Home's fees from their own resources.

D. Relatives, to relieve their guilt feelings, often react forcibly when their expectations of total care are not being realised and their parents are expected, within their assessed capacity, to undertake simple activities around the Home. They demand that their parents are "properly cared for.".

E. The care staff, domestic and kitchen staffs, influenced by their longer serving colleagues, see their own roles in terms of physical jobs to be done. They subscribe to the practice that it is far easier, for example, to tidy drawers themselves, than to stand by ready to give assistance whilst a resident attempts the task for herself. (A concept some Home Managers reinforce by creating the impression that staff are not properly employed unless they are working at recognisable tasks. 'Have you no proper work to do?' is an accusation not infrequently directed at a care assistant who is seated in a lounge talking to residents.)

F. The job descriptions of care staff list tasks which an outsider would feel lie more properly in the province of domestic staff; they neglect to include specific duties relating to the emotional and social needs of the residents.

G. Society persists with a duality in its standards, expecting residents to lead purposeful lives within the Home, yet being quick to criticise when an accident befalls one who has been encouraged to aim for a degree of independence.

H. Managers who are insecure in their own roles and ill-informed of management techniques fail to encourage junior staff to come forward with ideas to modify the internal organisation and routine of the home. This attitude denies the Home and the staff the chance to benefit from thoughtful interchange and confines the care staff to a task-orientated approach to completing basic routines. It is this approach to staff management that contributes to the frustration of care assistants when, flushed with new concepts obtained on study courses, they are met with the attitude 'I know what is best in this Home' or 'theory is for college; it won't work here.'

I. Official visitors (from voluntary homes management committees, councillors from SSDs, inexperienced inspectors, lay inspectors from inspection units, and relatives of potential residents) frequently concentrate their attentions during brief visits, on the state of the rooms, the cleanliness of surfaces and variety in the weekly menus. Seldom do they comment on the expressions on the faces of the residents the absence of recreational facilities or evidence of residents caring for themselves. Such visits only confirm the belief that those to whom the Home Manager is accountable are impressed solely by orderliness and good housekeeping.

J. Most Residential Homes adopt a policy of relying almost completely on part time, hourly paid workers as care assistants without considering the implications of such a policy. Whilst acknowledging that well-chosen part time staff have a valuable contribution to make, the policy has some serious disadvantages in the longer term. A staffing strategy based on hourly paid part time staff is usually associated with little or no formal training opportunities and the absence of a recognisable career structure for care staff. The basic grade staff therefore have little motivation to improve their skills and the organisation further denies itself by foregoing the benefits of being able to develop care staff, with potential, for more senior positions. It is for this reason that so many Home Managers are selected from allied professions and have not experienced the full range of work in residential care.

K. The assessment of residents in Homes is no less important than the assessment of children in care. Without assessment no treatment programmes can be devised, but the elderly residents who get regular assessment are the fortunate few. As a result individual capacities for self help frequently go unnoticed and the same blanket care is given to all.

Given the continuing influence of these factors -- and the list is by no means a comprehensive one -- the primary aim of a residential home for the elderly will remain substantially unmet, awaiting a spirited attack on the management of the Homes. An injection of extra money into the residential services would enable an increase in staffing hours and perhaps this is needed. Without this unlikely stimulant the standards of care may be improved by a more efficient utilisation of existing resources. This the Home Managers can achieve for themselves.

1.2 Common human needs

Before attempting to effect changes designed to improve the quality of life within the Home, the Manager would be advised to think in an organised fashion about the nature of human needs. For it is these needs that should dictate the objectives of the Home and which can be harnessed to motivate the staff to work towards the achievement of these objectives.

Abraham Maslow designed a model of human needs as a means of illustrating their hierarchical arrangement and perceiving their relationships one with another. From a simplification of this model we can gain an initial insight into the motivating force behind our behaviour and the origin of our frustrations.

Maslow arranged human needs into related groups which he then positioned in pyramidal strata with the most fundamental needs occupying the base of the pyramid and the others arranged in ascending order of sophistication, culminating in our psychological needs at the apex.

MASLOW'S HIERARCHY OF NEEDS

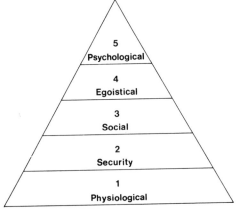

1. *Physiological needs.* In this, the lowest strata, are grouped those needs that are essential to sustain our biological life. They include the need for food, warmth, shelter, sleep and sexual expression. As long as these needs remain unmet they provide the motivating force for our behaviour with the activity being determined by the quest for their satiation. Once satisfied, however, they no longer serve as active motivators, they lie dormant and our behaviour becomes governed by the next level of needs which then emerge into consciousness.

2. *Security needs.* This level of needs makes us anxious to protect ourselves against personal danger and from threatened deprivation of food, shelter, and sexual expression. Under the influence of these needs our behaviour is motivated towards protecting those resources that will supply our future physiological requirements, stimulating us to maintain regular employment, save money, pay insurance premiums and contribute to pension schemes.

The continuing development of a welfare state, to protect vulnerable individuals from deprivation of this kind, is a genuine response to the pressures created by our safety needs.

3. *Social needs* occupying the third tier in Maslow's hierarchy, only serve to motivate our behaviour when our physiological and safety levels have been satisfied. Once secure in the comfortable assurance that we will not have our physiological needs threatened we become activated by our social needs; we select the company of others, choose to participate in communal activities, wish to reciprocate friendships and seek to foster a feeling of social belonging.

4. *Egoistical needs* become apparent only when we have satisfied our social ones and arise as a consequence of our inter-personal relationships. From social intercourse stems our awareness of self esteem; our desire to develop a sense of achievement, to become appreciated by others, and acquire status in the eyes of our fellows. This status need not always manifest itself in power, high social position or substantial material possessions. It is often sufficient to satisfy our self-respect for us to feel valued as individuals with a recognisable role in society.

5. *Psychological needs.* When we have achieved an established, if not exalted, position in society the motivating force of behaviour is provided no longer by the search for self-esteem, but by the power of emergent psychological needs. These needs Maslow places in the highest strata of his hierarchy, defining them in terms of our desire for personal growth and development. To use those talents we possess for creative purpose, to become accomplished in our own sphere, thus satisfying our inner-self.

From this model can be recognised both the nature of the needs that govern our behaviour and the sequence in which they operate. With dissatisfied needs continuing to direct our energies until they are satisfied, blocking the effects of higher needs, and satisfied needs no longer remaining effective motivators, allowing higher needs to function. (Even the tastiest dish will not tempt a person with a full stomach; or the offer of social status attract the starving one.) This is not to imply that there is no overlap between each category of need or that each group of needs has the same demand on all people, but exceptions, such as some creative artists, only underline the general principles expressed in Maslow's model.

We are never able to satisfy our needs completely, for with the satiation of one arises the hunger of the next. We behave according to the dictates of the need which is operative at the time and so we are constantly active.

Should our activity fail to satisfy totally or partially our presenting need, then we experience frustration of a type which reflects the nature of our unfilled need, in a strength proportional to its lack of satisfaction. Thus when our physiological needs are temporarily denied we feel hungry and cold - starvation only following a prolonged period of denial. When our safety needs are not being satisfied we become at first apprehensive then frightened; and when our higher needs are unfilled we feel emotionally frustrated. If this emotional frustration is for a short period only then it stimulates our efforts to satisfy the need, but if the need continues to be unmet despite our determined activity, then the frustration may have serious implications for our personality. For instance if we continually fail to develop friendships there is a strong likelihood that we will withdraw from close contact with others, in case we meet with similar rebuffs. Likewise if we are constantly unable to gain a sense of achievement through lack of suitable opportunity, suffering damage to our ego in consequence, we are in danger of losing our self-respect and becoming embittered.

Because of the importance of these needs to us all it is essential that any Manager of a Residential Home is fully conversant with their functioning, for her work is with people; people such as her residents who depend on her knowledge in this field to be able to satisfy their own needs; people such as her staff whose needs she must recognise to provide motivation for their work; people such as her management committee, visitors, volunteers and professional colleagues who are all responding to the force of their internal drives.

These needs are common to all people, but only the residents must find the means of satisfying them primarily within the Home, or suffer the effects of continual frustration. Let us then go over these needs again and relate them specifically to the lives of the residents examining the extent to which they are being met or remaining a source of frustration.

1. *Physiological needs.* There is usually a plentiful supply of wholesome food in all the Homes, with meal times forming the focal points of the daily routine. The Homes are warm, often to the extent of providing a soporific atmosphere, and bedrooms, if not affording privacy, certainly provide comfort and shelter. Physiological needs are generally being adequately met, with the possible exception of sexual expression.

2. *Security needs.* Although at first sight it would seem that the security needs of residents are being adequately met, in that nothing appears to threaten the means of meeting their future physiological needs, a more critical examination may reveal a less happy situation. Apart from those few lucky individuals, sound in mind and financial status, who can move themselves from one Private Residential Home to another, many residents may face real or imagined threat. Indeed even these fortunate few must think ahead to the time when longevity and inflation will have eroded their financial independence.

It is still the common practice in many organisations to require new residents to surrender their pension books to the administration staff, receiving in return their statutory weekly allowance. This practice is defended, not only for the purpose of the administrative convenience, but because it is deemed that many residents are quite unable to cash their order forms for themselves, or if able to do so they would be reluctant to pay the required weekly payments towards their maintenance at the Home. These arguments are valid in some cases, but by no means all, and it is a subject to which we must return. Suffice it to illustrate for the moment that in this one respect the residents are denied a simple safety need to feel financially secure.

The pension book is still regarded by most old people living independent lives in their own homes as their guarantee of a weekly income. Even though new residents may be assured that they have a home and security for life, the forceful removal of their own pension book is seen by many as a deprivation, an inroad into their independence, a loss felt deeply yet seldom complained of.

Those residents who were fortunate enough to own their own homes or have protection of tenure are made to relinquish this security factor within a very short time of coming in to care. Again it would be properly argued that this is a necessary measure in the circumstances. But the frail elderly may see the possession of their own home as a means of safeguarding their future needs or a valuable asset to be willed to relatives. In the act of relinquishing their own homes they are being robbed of their independence and thrown completely on the mercy of those who control the Residential Home.

Security needs of residents are additionally and frequently threatened by agreements between the Health and Social Service Departments concerning the admission to hospital wards of those who fall ill with anything other than an acute temporary illness. This agreement pronounces that before one resident can take up a hospital bed the home has to accept a patient in return -- a pernicious 'one for one swap'. Not only does this affect the resident, when in hospital she learns that her bed is being occupied by a stranger, but equally affects the remaining residents who, witnessing the scene, feel threatened themselves. They may then resolve to hide, as far as possible, from the care staff any symptoms they develop, the discovery of which may result in their transfer to hospital.

Security needs are sometimes challenged by the actions of the caring staff themselves. For example, whenever care assistants, in an attempt to persuade a difficult resident to adopt a more agreeable disposition, say, in a volume to be overheard by others, 'If you cannot learn to behave yourself and stop being a trouble, you will have to go. We haven't the time to keep bothering with residents who continually upset other people.' These words quite often produce the desired effect, the resident duly conforms thinking 'where would I go if I left here, I've sold my home and my relatives won't have me anymore?' But what is the cost, not only to the resident, but to others who witness these scenes? The cost is enormously high and paid in the currency of human unhappiness.

The persuasive statements that Social Workers use when convincing reluctant clients to accept residential accommodation and the welcoming words of the Home Manager, when receiving the client into care, would seem to bode well for the future, assuring the old person of a secure and independent residence. But would the picture freely painted by existing residents in their own perspectives be so rosy, or would it show life in the Home to contain many threats to personal security?

Residents are often conscious of the state of their security needs, yet can do little to remedy the situation. The frustration generated by this deprivation begins to affect their personality, facilitating the process of socialisation into the Home and resulting in the stereotyped behavioural pattern so characteristic of institutional neurosis. The residents' quiet acceptance of the Home's regime when born of the need to conform to the staff's expectations, cannot be taken as an indication that their security needs are being properly catered for.

3. *Social needs.* Few would dispute the existence of our social needs that drive us to seek the company of others, to develop a sense of belonging and make friendships. So much do we acknowledge the importance of these needs that we feel deeply for those who for one reason or another are unable

to socialise and we feel compelled to help. It is consideration of these needs that prompts well-intentioned people to persuade the elderly into Residential Homes with the words 'you will have the company of others all day, people to talk to, new friendships to make. It's lonely where you live now and you know it.' Whether or not this expectation will be realised depends on the nature of the Home and the degree of stimulation to be found within it.

An unobtrusive glance through the doors of most lounges seldom reveals the signs of social interaction. In some of the Homes with smaller lounges there may be the occasional friendship that leads to some semblance of conversation, but in most lounges there is an observable lack of verbal communication. A kind of quietness pervades the atmosphere, punctuated by the infrequent visits of members of staff as they serve the afternoon teas, summon someone for a bath or escort a resident to the toilet. On these occasions the staff may have a jolly word to say, a question to ask, or a joke to relate, that temporarily animates the residents, but on their departure the silence is resumed and bored expressions tend to assume their habitual lines.

That the residents do not care for social intercourse is just not true. Witness what happens when a talkative visitor enters a lounge prepared to embrace all present in his conversation; note how many residents come to life, vie for attention or just listen appreciatively; observe how disappointed they appear when, because of the numerous demands placed on the visitor's attendance, only a few can have their conversations reciprocated; see how quickly the lounge subsides when the visitor leaves, with just an odd comment made by a resident to no one in particular, 'What a nice young man! Was he from the Welfare?'

It may be said that the residents respond like this because they find a new face or different voice particularly stimulating. Undoubtedly this is so, but should the contrast between life in the room before the visitor enters and the atmosphere whilst he is there, be so stark, and does this comparison not reveal the almost lack of social interaction that reigns in so many of our homes? Surely it is not sufficient to explain this phenomenon by suggesting the residents see so much of each other that they have nothing to talk about. If they have nothing to talk about it is because so little happens to cause interest, let alone excitement when left to their own devices. Institutionalisation breeds boredom and inertia which are self-perpetuating. This would explain why, when a rare excursion is arranged from the Home and the time comes to depart, so many of the residents exhibit little enthusiasm for the visit preferring to stay at Home. (Did they previously agree to go so as not to offend the manager?)

These examples suggest that although we accept the importance of social needs to our personal well-being there is in Residential Homes little facility for residents to satisfy theirs.

4. *Egoistical needs.* It is our egoistical needs that motivate our behaviour towards obtaining the esteem and recognition from which we derive our status in our community. No one can hold up his head for long, feel wanted and exude confidence unless he is frequently assured of recognition from those with whom he associates that he is valued for his rights, as well as his obligations, and is seen as a distinct personality with a role to play in the group.

Hence our objections to being treated as numbers, our dislike of bureaucracy and any organisational procedures that do not identify us as people.

These needs are equally significant to the inmates of residential homes for the elderly, yet to what extent are they met? Do we, in fact, accord to our residents the status they deserve or are we tempted to assume, because they have been admitted to our care, we can dispense with the privileges we would never dream of withholding from persons outside?

In society we sense our status by the way people respond to us as individuals; the way they react in our presence, the words they select, how they deliver them and their general disposition towards us.

Consider your approach to a child, an adult, the milkman or mayor. (The milkman and mayor may be one and the same person but when he is robed the chances are you will behave differently than when you meet him with his bottles and float.) Unless you are a most unusual type of person who not only claims to treat everyone the same way but actually does so, you will by your voice and body language, betray your assumption of a person's standing. You will do so subconsciously - your behaviour being the result of your socialisation as a child and you will be unaware of your reaction unless it is brought to your attention. We are conditioned to react in approved ways and people measure from our reactions the status we have accorded them.

Applying this to our residents, how many times do we address an elderly person in plural terms, such as, 'Isn't it time we were in bed?' A form of address we might use to a child, but certainly not to an adult.

Similarly we pat residents on the head as we walk past them, uttering a few casual words of address. We fail to knock on bedroom doors before we enter or, equally objectionably, we knock and then enter without even a pause to catch any reply. In effect we signal that we feel our status as staff so superior to that of the residents we can intrude on their privacy with impunity.

Care staff will call from one end of a lounge to a man in a distant corner that it is his bath time, announcing to the whole room a rather personal fact that could equally as effectively have been communicated to him much more intimately.

Apart from the shouting aloud, it is not an erosion of the personal status for an adult, even one living in a residential home, to be told it is his bathtime, rather than to suggest to him he could be assisted to bath if he wished.

In scores of similar ways we deny the residents of our Homes the common courtesies of adult life that we would automatically give to them if they lived elsewhere. The effect of the residents is of course to erode the esteem previously enjoyed as adult members of society and eventually to destroy their self-respect. To excuse this behaviour on the grounds that they are confused or 'just like children', is to blind ourselves to our real reasons. Residents who are treated in this manner are more readily contained in the home with a minimum of effort by the staff. People who are given rights and accorded real status are likely to demand that we exercise greater care and diligence in our personal contact with them, which of course increases the complexity of work.

5. *Psychological needs.* Our psychological needs, as previously outlined, include the desire for personal growth and development, the wish to become accomplished and creative. If, of course, our social and egoistical needs are constantly frustrated it is not surprising these psychological needs have their latent potential suppressed. It could be in the frustration of these lower needs that the apathy of so many residents has its origin, rather than in any intrinsic lack of necessary faculties.

On many occasions senior staff of residential homes complain they are unable to interest residents in creative activities; moan when they show reluctance to participate in any project a student on placement wishes to develop, or when they resist the overtures of a willing volunteer. This lack of interest they attribute to the age of the inmates, yet the picture is so different in day centres for the elderly. In these establishments elderly people, as old, or almost as old, as the residents of Homes and equally incapacitated with varying handicaps, happily produce a diversity of creations in the arts and crafts, which are so eagerly bought during sales of work.

Why then, if these elderly, handicapped clients in day centres can be actively creative in this way, obtaining from their activities considerable self-satisfaction, do we have such a problem with similar people who reside in our Homes? There is no glib answer to this question, for there are many factors to be considered when comparing the two establishments. Day centres employ staff to be predominantly concerned with the emotional welfare of the clients, rather than catering for their physical needs which admittedly are not so demanding in a day care service; whereas staff in Homes providing twenty-four hour support are involved with dressing residents, laying tables, serving meals, toiletting, bathing, bed-making and laundry work-tasks, their counter-parts in the day centres are essentially free from these routines.

Day centre staff are therefore at liberty to concentrate on making conversation, arranging social activities and equipping clients with materials for creative work. In day centres of the better kind there is, therefore, an atmosphere of purposefulness; staff and clients co-operating to achieve goals in a way that is so blatantly missing from our Homes. An additional time factor contributes as well to differences in the two establishments. In day centres the clients go home at the end of the their day. By doing so they take new community experience home with them, which builds confidence, independence and social awareness so difficult to achieve in full time residence.

Differences between day clients and residents can also be observed in those residential homes that provide day care facilities. The willingness to converse and the general alertness of the day care clients contrast starkly with the attitudes of the permanent residents. But note how quickly these differences, once so markedly apparent, evaporate when full-time residence is assumed by former day clients. No one who has observed this metamorphosis can honestly doubt that it is the permanency of residence which so speedily brings about the change. Yet the cause of the change is not consciously accepted by the majority of the staff who refer to the transformation as 'settling in'. When a resident, who before her admission led a reasonably independent life, shows her resentment of the regime of the Home by being vocal in her objections and stubbornly resisting the pressures to conform, she is labelled as 'difficult'. The staff say she is taking time to 'settle in'. Later when the power of the institution has weighed down quietly upon her and she, like the established residents, no longer reacts against the routine, regulations and expectations of the Home, she becomes in the eyes of the staff, 'nicely settled'.

Residents in Homes are seldom expected to be creative, to have a purpose in life or to develop a sense of achievement, and because this expectation is not present the appropriate opportunities to meet the psychological needs are not made available. These needs eventually become suppressed, through the lack of opportunity for expression, thus reinforcing the staff's view that elderly residents are not interested in doing for themselves and thereby confirming their original expectation. In these conditions the psychological needs remain not only dormant, but frustrated, and although the frustration may not manifest itself in behavioural changes easily associated with the cause, it makes a significant contribution to the atmosphere in the homes.

The value of studying Maslow's hierarchy of human need lies in making us aware of the diversity of needs we all share, how they operate and the results of failure to satisfy them. When we superimpose these needs on to the life style of our residents, we begin to appreciate how little opportunity exists for their satisfaction and how easily they can be ignored by the staff.

Taken at face value, Residential Homes seem to cater well for the residents, but a more critical observation reveals that their resources are directed at the physiological level, leaving the higher strata of need in a state of neglect. Home Managers may retort, with a measure of justification, that low staffing quotas, imposed by commercial considerations, militate against the provision of a more stimulating environment, for with staff fully employed at their routine domestic tasks 'spare' time is at a premium and no hours seem available for diversional activities to relieve the monotony of life. If this were the true situation there would appear to be little hope for improving the quality of life in the Homes, but there is fortunately contrary evidence.

Comparison between Homes of similar size, structure, staffing ratios and residents' capabilities does not reveal similarity in standards of care. Some Homes try to impose, by one means or another, fixed retiring and raising times, rigid daily routines, predictable meals and resident contact by the care staff reduced to that necessitated with the demands of physical functions. In such Homes the residents display the typical symptoms of institutionalised life - expressionless faces, mental inertia, stooping gait and physical lethargy.

In other Homes some of the residents (if not all) are encouraged to make decisions for themselves, arise when they wish, make menu selections at lunchtime, look after their own rooms, control the spending of the comforts fund and participate in outside visits. The staff, whilst attending to basic tasks, enjoy considerable contact with the residents whom they respond to as individuals and in the Home they help provide a rich experience of activities.

If the establishments observed have approximately equal resources then the explanations of the disparity must lie in the management techniques employed by the Home Manager; the objectives she has set relating the work of the Home to the needs of the residents, the way she deploys her staff and her success in motivating them to meet these objectives.

CHAPTER 2
The Residents

Knowledge of human need is the basis on which a Home Manager can begin to build a caring environment. From this knowledge she can formulate objectives for the Home which will reflect the standards of care she aspires to. But the Home Manager, in common with all other managers, can only determine standards for her organisation, not achieve them by herself; she must realise the objectives through the work of the staff. In the role as Manager she must become aware of residents' needs, translate these needs into objectives, convey the objectives to the staff, motivate them towards their attainment and constantly appraise the objectives as the changing circumstances of the residents dictate.

2.1 Setting Objectives for a Home

We have examined the nature of human need; what now are objectives?

'Aims', 'objectives', 'targets' and 'goals' are words commonly employed in managerial exercises, but they are not synonyms and their meanings are frequently confused for want of clearer understandings. The terms 'goals' and 'targets' we may disregard as being more appropriate words for industry and commerce and concentrate our attention on 'aims' and 'objectives' which are perhaps more suitable terms for the field of residential care. We may appreciate the benefits accruing from the employment of objectives if first we have a better understanding of what they are and how they contrast with a more generalised aim.

An aim is a general term that denotes a direction of purpose for an individual or organisation to pursue, but it does not detail a definite end point. An objective is more precise in that it relates to a clearly defined achievement. The two together are complementary, but an aim without objectives is of questionable value.

These principles defining aims and objectives can be used to good advantage in the management of residential homes for the elderly. If a Home Manager simply perceives for the organisation a generalised philosophy, for example, 'to provide a caring environment in which elderly people can lead, as far as is practical, an independent life' and fails to support it with more precise objectives, all that will be established is a general direction for the Home. This will convey little to those involved with her in running the Home. What are the staff to understand by a 'caring environment' or 'an independent life'? Yet many Managers when asked to state the purpose of their Homes are content to speak in generalities. They deny themselves the opportunity of setting specific standards of care and in consequence cannot monitor the effect of their Homes on the residents, evaluate the relative merits and expertise of their individual staff, or assess their own personal performance as Managers.

No one would argue with the philosophy of an objective that stated 'to create a happy, relaxed atmosphere in which the residents can feel at ease' as it embodies a worthy sentiment. The argument against it lies in its vagueness. How, as an objective, would it be conveyed to the staff, how would they set about reaching it or know when they had? To be of working value objectives must relate to tasks than can be performed and assessed and be written in words free of ambiguity. When writing such objectives care is needed to avoid expressions describing the atmosphere of the Home (happy, content, peaceful, homely etc), or the attitude of mind of the residents (independent, social, stimulated) or other equally intangible factors. Valuable qualities though they may be, their distinctly subjective nature makes them unsatisfactory as objectives, difficult to convey to the staff and almost impossible to assess in a practical situation.

If a manager wishes to incorporate these qualities in the philosophy of her Home, then they can be encapsulated in her aim which describes the general direction of the establishment, for this is where they should properly reside. For example the words 'to meet the emotional, social, physical needs of the elderly frail in a homely environment which respects their independence, protects their status as adults and encourages their individuality' would be quite acceptable in an aim. The Home Manager may use whatever expressions she personally prefers to outline the philosophy of the Home; in her objectives however she must be more precise if they are to serve the functions previously ascribed to them. They are formulated by her for personal use and the guidance of the staff, it is not intended for them to be broadcast beyond the Home. Therefore the words she uses should be selected to relate to practical functions, not to portray a public image.

The objectives listed below are given only as examples to stimulate thought. They do not constitute a comprehensive list and it is not suggested that they are all appropriate to every circumstance. An assumption is made that the Home will equip itself with attractive furnishings, provide wholesome regular meals and attend to the physical functions of the residents. The objectives are designed for the specific purpose of improving existing standards of care and promoting more efficient use of care staff.

1. To assess each resident within a week of admission to determine her capacity for self-help.

2. To devise treatment programmes for each resident based on the results of assessment.

3. To re-assess each resident at six monthly intervals and revise treatment programmes as indicated.

4. To observe and record each resident's performance in respect of her treatment programme.

5. To arrange work rotas for the care staff that include periods devoted to actual resident contact.

6. To form a resident's committee responsible for the administration of the Home's 'comforts' funds.

7. To allow residents to decide for themselves when they will rise in the morning or retire at night.

8. To give residents discretion when and if they will bathe.

9. To provide a menu that offers a selection of food at lunchtime.

10. To assist residents who have the ability to control their financial affairs to make arrangements for the collection of their pension and the payment of monies to the authority.

11. To provide materials for a minimum of ten separate recreational activities, in consultation with the residents.

12. To organise a minimum of six excursions each year, as agreed with the residents.

13. To provide residents with the facilities to help themselves to hot drinks.

14. To recruit a body of volunteers who will assist with the provision of recreational activities.

15. To require care staff to be familiar with the history of residents in their care.

16. To hold fortnightly meetings at which all grades of staff may discuss matters arising from the work of the home.

Devising objectives in this manner is not as difficult as making them work. That people, for instance, who enter residential care should have their relative deficiencies and capabilities assessed so the Home may react positively to their needs, is self-evident. How this is to be accomplished in Homes for the elderly is quite another matter. On-going assessment of children in residential care is rigidly controlled by regulations, but similar provision is not made for old people who may live for a decade or more in a Home. The following section on assessment and activity programmes is designed to assist with this particular problem.

One way in which residents can be relieved of pursuing an institution-alising daily time-table is to permit them to decide the time they will rise each morning. (Observers are often perturbed to discover how early elderly people are required to rise in our Homes, especially when they can discover nothing of urgency in the ensuing day's activities). Managers, however, are often committed to their residents rising early, since dressing them is a function of night staff (something a little inconsistent in itself) and breakfast is at a fixed time to accommodate the duty of the cook, who must supervise the washing of the morning's dirty crockery and prepare luncheon for noon. Initially the anticipated effects on the Home's routine of some residents arising later than a pre-determined hour would be sufficient to deter many Managers from accepting this objective. Yet its implementation need not cause such disturbance if, for instance, it is restricted to those residents who can dress themselves and who properly understand the result of missing a cooked breakfast is to help themselves to a bowl of cereals. By the simple expedient of setting aside one table laid with cereals, sugar and milk (a toaster would be an embellishment), at least some residents could avail themselves of an otherwise seemingly impossible variance in routine.

In a similar vein the provision of the means for residents to enjoy hot drinks, other than when distributed by the staff, may appear as an unobtainable idea. Kettles of boiling water are without doubt dangerous to the confused or unwieldy to the arthritic, but not all residents are so handicapped and for them tea-making facilities could be provided. For the rest, an urn or large thermos flasks would suffice, even if this means more lucid and ambulant residents pouring the drinks for their less fortunate colleagues.

To offer a choice of food at lunchtime may be prohibited on a basis of cost, unless the choice is between, say, soup and main course, or main course and sweet. If only half the number of soups and sweets are prepared to the number of lunches cooked then the cost is simply a little extra work in the kitchens. The residents would benefit enormously. Of course some residents will prefer a sweet, when all sweets have been served and have to be content with a soup; others may demand a sweet they did not previously request and have to learn how the system works; yet others, in their confusion, may never appreciate a choice exists and have to have the selection made for them. These are negative arguments to advance against the implementation of the objective, but they are not insurmountable hurdles and can be overcome by a determined approach. Lunchtimes may be a little less quiet, but where there is noise there is certainly life.

Mealtimes assume such a significant role in the life of the residents that their organisation deserves a greater consideration than it frequently receives. Mealtimes are valued by the residents not for any stimulating or convivial contributions they make to life in the home, but simply for their anticipatory value. They are something to look forward to, a break from the monotony of life in the lounges. However when all meals are shared by all residents, using the one room at the same time, the act of dining can become nothing more than the change of one routine activity for another, thus contributing to the growth of institutional neurosis.

Late breakfast facilities and menu choices can introduce a little variety to dining but much more can be achieved by questioning the whole dining arrangements. Is it really necessary for luncheon always to be served in the dining room? Would an occasional meal taken more privately add a fill-up to life? How can variety be introduced to mitigate the effects of continuous communal eating?

Few Homes are devoid of some available space -- a visitors room, an uncrowded lounge, or a partly enclosed area beside a stairway -- that could accommodate a few residents for a meal away from the main body of diners on a special occasion. Here a table could be laid with an attractive cloth, and set with separate cutlery and crockery, for a resident to enjoy a birthday meal with her chosen friends. Indeed their popularity may make it difficult to resist extending them to involve all (or all capable) residents on a rota basis more frequent than their birthdays. Where there exists more than one suitable dining area several groups could simultaneously enjoy the benefits of more private meals.

The delivery of food and the return of used dishes need not present any problems, particularly when the floors are level between the kitchen and dining area. A loaded trolley could be collected from the kitchen and returned at the end of the meal, preferably by one of the diners. The purchase of a 'hostess' trolley for this purpose should be viewed as a wise investment not an extravagant expenditure.

The development of separate dining arrangements like this could be a useful way of assessing the capabilities of the more ambulant residents for a degree of group living, where a small number of residents would take most, if not all, of their meals together. If the Home is of a design with small lounges, a lounge could serve as a base for the group, or alternatively another area used.

To return to the topic of objectives and the question of their implementation. By offering some residents the opportunity to exercise limited discretion, to take decisions on personal matters or to vary their daily routine, when other residents are incapable of doing so, is not to practice favouritism but to respond positively to needs.

No Manager, however much consideration she applies, can formulate objectives that will be simple to achieve. Naturally the residents are individual and no single system can be made to apply to them all. But, without definite objectives, a Manager is unlikely to improve the standard of care, utilise her staff fully, or be able to assess the achievements of her Home. If objectives are treated as servants not obeyed as masters, made flexible to suit the Home with its varying individuals and constantly appraised, then there is much to commend their adoption. The extra work involved in devising them will be repaid in abundance.

It may be the Manager's wish to adopt as objectives activities precluded by local regulations, staff shortages, or the lack of facilities or finance. Then the objectives may have to await a more favourable climate. Indeed, in some Homes only the more fundamental objectives may be realisable at first with more significant progress emerging in gradual stages.

2.2 Assessment of Residents

Unless great care is taken to protect the independence of new arrivals, the Home can quickly extinguish the remaining flames of self-sufficiency and independence. The total provision of physical care, whether or not needed by the resident, is a comfortable temptation.

Institutionalisation of residents often commences with the attitude of placement officers or close relatives when they describe how care staff will cater for the elderly person's every need. In this way the concept of total care is seeded in the minds of the old person, which, should she accept the move into care can be nurtured by the Manager. 'Welcome to our Home. I know you will be happy here. Everyone is. There's nothing to be unhappy about. If you want anything just ask, but I don't think you will want much.'

The staff not infrequently continue the growth of the process by saying: 'We have to dress you early each morning - to get you downstairs. Cook has made breakfast and the domestics need to tidy your room.' If the new resident still harbours doubts concerning her intended role in the Home they will be quickly dispersed by her fellow at breakfast. 'Don't move the pots. They will have us all helping if you do -- it's their job you know. That's what they are paid for.'

17

Statements such as these are repeated to scores of new residents each year. Unable or unwilling to resist the pressures placed upon them, the new arrivals quickly assume the characteristics of an institutionalised personalities, depending upon others for the satisfaction of their needs.

It will no doubt be argued by some Managers that with severe competition for new residents,(a factor particularly important to the private sector), that market forces require Homes to respond to the demands of those who place residents. Managers are aware that many relatives convince themselves that their elderly relative needs complete care. Such relatives then seek to assuage their guilt in not providing this care themselves by securing a place in a Home that will. If the Home subsequently is seen to be encouraging the relative to participate in life's activities and the resident is responding well to this encouragement, then the relatives' self-convinced reason for placing their relative evaporates, to their discomfort.

Managers respond to this predicament by stressing in their marketing literature just how well total care will be provided, then respond to their own words. In doing this, for short term gain, they sacrifice the greater commercial advantage of quality care tailored to individual needs. Homes where residents are treated as individuals, encouraged to be active commensurate with their abilities, given decisions to make and choices to take, exude an atmosphere of quality that is readily sensed by those assessing the Home for future use.

Old people living alone, even in the poorest conditions, are constantly faced with decisions to make and tasks to perform. Decisions affecting when to get up in the mornings, what to eat for breakfast, how to get the shopping done; tasks like struggling to dress, buttering bread and washing dishes; mental and physical activities which collectively keep the brain working, the mind orientated and the body active. Admittedly residents who are taken into care have reached the stage where they no longer are able to cope adequately with maintaining an independent life, but few have deteriorated to a point where they can do nothing for themselves. Yet once in residential care they are all too often presented with a sterile routine of total care, unrelieved by any necessity to provide for themselves. The twin therapies of movement and thought which in the life of residents prior to their admission did so much to maintain their physical and mental activity are displaced from this valuable function in residential establishments.

If regular assessment, which is a much neglected area with the elderly, received detailed attention, not just as a once and for all act in assessment centres, but as regular procedure in all Homes, then older people could be encouraged to play a more active role in caring for themselves, benefiting both emotionally and physically.

A possible assessment procedure would be to relate the capabilities of the residents to pre-selected activities within the Home. The activities chosen depending upon the available facilities within the Home, the anticipated capabilities of residents, the ambitions of the care staff, and the degree of general co-operation forthcoming from other workers in the Home. It may be necessary at first, as with the adoption of stated objectives, to begin in a small way, developing in complexity as experience and confidence allows. The following areas may be ample to start with:

Dressing/undressing
Bathing
Meals
Room care
Domestic work
Accommodation fees
Medication
Recreational activities

The activities which are selected could be displayed on simple assessment sheets [See Tables I & II on pages 22 & 23 following for examples] with sufficient space provided against each activity for a detailed comment. When completed these assessment sheets would present an accurate profile of all residents, reflecting individual capabilities and indicating any necessary modifications required to assist them to lead more independent lives. From this assessment information the Home Manager and her care team could devise an 'activity programme' for all residents which would be in keeping with their capacity for self-help. When fully discussed with the residents, to ensure they all understand what will be expected of them, the activity programmes could be attached to the assessment sheets and made freely available to all the staff who would be required to familiarise themselves with the expectations the Home had for each resident. (This internal assessment procedure would be quite separate from the confidential case files which accompany each resident into care, and would not contain any sensitive information the Home Manager would be unhappy to divulge openly to the staff.) Ideally the initial assessment of residents should be completed before admission to the Home or shortly afterwards, so that each resident is quickly involved in a degree of self-care before she has time to succumb to a life style of non-participation.

Whatever approach is adopted in the assessment of residents and the design of activity programmes, the system must have sufficient inbuilt flexibility to accommodate periods of illness or other indications that the activity programmes should be temporarily suspended. There will be occasions when residents have quite genuine difficulty with certain activities. At these times the staff must be at hand to give willing help or encouragement; at other times some residents may refuse to co-operate simply because they are not in the mood, and care staff must be able to discriminate between the two conditions. Regular re-assessments will be required throughout the year to ensure each activity programme still reflects the capabilities of the residents, for though some may improve noticeably in the early months of their residence as a result of good care, a gradual deterioration in the general condition of the residents is to be expected as they age.

Activity programmes cannot simulate the conditions of normal life in a family home. Indeed they are not intended to do so, since elderly people come into care primarily because they are unable to support themselves at home. But such programmes could go a long way towards restoring to residents a little dignity and purpose by increasing their independence.

Any innovation that interferes with the established routine of the Home will not go unchallenged and the introduction of assessment, linked to activity programmes, will have its attendant difficulties. The wise manager will anticipate these, with a view to either discovering solutions or finding ways to contain them without interfering with the success of the scheme.

For instance, some of the residents may be so accustomed to their lives of relative immobility that any attempts to involve them in prescribed activities will fail to arouse their interest, or will cause them to become deliberately obstructive. In such cases attention should be concentrated on their more co-operative colleagues and those newly admitted, since the advantages of activity programmes to the majority should not be lost for want of complete involvement.

Several residents will be suffering from degrees of confusion of physical handicap which will prevent their participation. This again should not detract from the value of the project to the more lucid and ambulant residents.

An objection may be raised by relatives who misunderstand the purpose of the Home and feel that it exists to provide total care for their parent who should under no circumstances be called upon to do 'work' for the staff. To these people it needs to be explained that the aim of these activities is not to relieve the staff of work -- indeed these activities place increased demands on the care assistants -- but to provide a realistic means of preserving the mental and physical agility of the residents. This objection would probably not be raised if, when admission was being considered, both the resident and her relatives were informed of the objectives of the Home, the reasons for the assessment and the principles underlining activity programmes. Discussion beforehand could do much to allay any fears of exploitation and prepare the resident herself for co-operation in a scheme designed to maintain her health, privacy and independence.

Resistance to implementation of the scheme may also be forthcoming from members of the staff who anticipate an increase in the complexity of their work load without a corresponding rise in remuneration; or simply because they distrust any idea that involves changes and suspect management of ulterior motives.

No Home Manager could expect any success with a scheme that did not carry the wholehearted support of the majority of the staff, on whose enthusiasm and support she must depend. Staff who feel threatened by proposed changes of this nature have their anxiety based in lack of understanding. From the moment the Manager resolves to introduce assessment with activity programmes into the Home she would be well advised to hold a series of staff meetings during which she could explain her desires and listen to the reservations of her colleagues and hopefully hear their suggestions. Care staff frequently complain, during in-service training courses, that they are seldom taken into the confidence of management and say they would welcome more opportunity to discuss life in the home with senior staff.

There is undoubtedly a considerable pool of goodwill and untapped potential amongst the care staff that could be harnessed in this way, given suitable encouragement. Though there will be some who lack professional commitment and who will have to be 'carried' by the rest, the benefits that regular assessments promise should not be sacrificed for want of total staff approval.

TABLE I

ASSESSMENT DETAILS

Name: Mrs X   Age: 81 (+ date of birth)

Date admitted: 24.5.95

Assessed by: Mrs Y and Miss Z

Date assessed: 1.6.95 (initial)

Dressing: Mrs X can undress and dress herself slowly, but has difficulty in fastening small buttons and in coping with her tights. Unable to tie laces properly on shoes.

Bathing : Can undress herself, but requires steadying in and out of the bath. Needs help to dry thoroughly afterwards but will dress afterwards.

Meals: No special dietary requirements - feeds herself well.

Room care: Able to make bed, but not well. Can clean washbasin and polish surfaces. Can attend to tidiness of wardrobe and drawers.

Domestic work: Willingly helped with table laying. Buttered bread without difficulty.

Accommodation Understands decimal money very well, and knows *fees:* amount of pension without prompting. Unable to collect pension because of difficulty walking outside. Daughter has previously done this.

Medication: No medication prescribed. Takes soluble aspirin for occasional headaches.

Recreational Expressed no recent involvement in any activities: Does not like knitting.

TABLE 2

ACTIVITY PROGRAMME

Name: Mrs X   Assessment date: 1.6.95 (initial)

Dressing: All clothes to have small buttons replaced with Velcro fastenings except her best blouses. To be shown how to use stocking aid. To dress and undress herself, except when wearing laced shoes when she will need help.

Bathing: To undress herself, but requires help into bath.Will wash thoroughly, but ring for assistance to get out of bath and for drying. To dress herself.

Meals: No help required. Will take late breakfast at discretion. Check in mornings to observe.

Room care: Provide with continental quilt. To make own bed, polish surfaces and clean washbasin. To attend to drawers and wardrobe. Domestic staff to polish floor and check surfaces weekly.

Domestic work: To join table-laying and bread buttering rotas.

Accommodation Daughter to cash pension weekly. Mrs X to pay fees to Duty Manager or deputy on Fridays.

Medication: To collect bottle of five soluble aspirins for personal use from duty manager. Issues to be noted.

Recreational activities: To be introduced to a range of activities available, no special interests.

CHAPTER 3
The Care Staff

When a person takes up a first appointment as the Manager of a residential home for the elderly a new career stage is embarked upon which requires functioning on quite a different plane. No longer will the individual be directly involved with attending to the personal care of residents, this being the task of the care staff; from now onwards the Manager must see to the wider needs of the residents, through the work of the staff/team. The whole essence of management lies in the achievement of objectives through the organised control of the work of others. Consequently when a Home fails to achieve its objectives -- provided these objectives have been carefully considered -- the reasons for failure invariably lie in the management of junior staff, for which the Home Manager must accept responsibility and seek a remedy in the management techniques employed.

Any Manager who answers criticism of the standards of care in the home by commenting upon the negative attitude of the staff, their readiness to quote job descriptions when invited to take part in new activities, their reluctance to attend staff meetings outside normal working hours or their prime motive for working being their weekly wage packet, is describing personal deficiencies as a manager of the Home. Either the staff has been badly selected, or the objectives of the Home have not been properly communicated or the Manager is unable to motivate them adequately. These factors of motivation, communication and selection must form the essential elements of staff management.

3.1 The motivations of staff

'What more do they want?' 'Are they never satisfied?' 'All they think about is money and they won't give a fair day's work for what they get.'

These words are repeated time and again by managers everywhere, who in moments of exasperation disclose how little they appreciate the complexity of human motivation. There is no simple answer to the question why some people work well and others indifferently -- though volumes have been written on the subject -- but some knowledge of motivating factors is essential to all who wish to succeed in the management of workers.

In the previous section we examined Maslow's hierarchy of human needs as a model for understanding the needs of residents. We saw how human needs could be categorised, with higher needs remaining dormant until lower needs have been satisfied. Once a category of need has been satisfied it no longer serves as a motivating influence, leaving behaviour to be influenced by the next higher level.

In applying this theory to individuals at work we acknowledge that these needs attend a person whatever his situation. Employees do not leave behind their higher needs and take only their basic needs to their place of employment.

If we take Maslow's categories of need, as previously itemised in Chapter 1.2, we can attempt to translate them into words that signify the influence they may exert on behaviour at work.

Physiological needs. The need for food, warmth, sleep and sexual expression.

In our society we no longer attempt to meet our basic needs directly, instead we sell our daily labour in return for money with which to purchase the means of supporting our bodily requirements.

In the working situation this need is met by a person's wage; he works to obtain enough money to buy these essentials and as long as he feels short of them the prospect of additional money will motivate him to co-operate with his employer. However when he draws a wage sufficient for his needs as he sees them, the offer of greater payment diminishes in its effect as an incentive to work harder.

Security needs. The need for protection against threats to the continuing satisfaction of physiological needs.

At work the awareness of our safety needs urges us to remain in employment so that we may continue to draw our weekly wage or salary. To this end we attempt to satisfy our boss with our work and we avoid violating organisational rules that would result in our dismissal.

Although these safety needs are important motivators of behaviour at work, their effectiveness is reduced the more difficult it becomes to dismiss an employee. This becomes all the more apparent when the employee is not the only provider of a family's earnings (working spouse) and when welfare benefits ensure that physiological needs will not go wanting even if loss of work happens. Therefore when a person is confident that his employment with an organisation will continue, his pension rights remaining protected, then his safety needs will no longer provide his employer with a means to motivate him. Their influence on his behaviour will only return when the continuation of his regular employment is threatened as in cases of proposed redundancy.

Social needs. The need to participate in social activities, develop reciprocal friendships, become accepted by society to which there can be a sense of belonging.

The satisfaction of these needs in the working environment comes from our membership of a work force, being part of a team with a common aim with whom we can identify and become accepted as colleagues. From our work situation we seek also a means of forming wider social contacts and involving ourselves with the local community. (It is the loss of these non-fiscal rewards of regular employment that are sorely missed by the retired or unemployed.)

When management fails to allow situations to develop in which staff may satisfy their emergent social needs by feeling part of a team working towards shared objectives, then it denies itself access to a powerful incentive; at the same time encouraging staff to form groups on their own initiative. Invariably such groups form their own objectives, often in conflict with those of the organisation, leading to collective attempts at sabotage, limiting work output to enhance overtime payment or frustrating rationalisation plans designed to improve efficiency.

Although ample money and security of employment allows people to pursue their social needs outside working hours, this does not detract from the value of social needs as motivators in work. In fact many people are forced to demand more money to satisfy social needs in their leisure time, only because they cannot meet them at work.

Egoistical needs. The need to feel appreciated by others, recognised for our worth and accorded status in our community.

These needs arise as a result of our membership of a group of people and apply with equal force whether we are at home or in work. In the context of our employment they exhibit themselves as our desire to feel valued by our co-workers for the role we play in the team and praised by our superiors for our contribution to the organisation. From this acceptance we gain status at work on which to build our self-esteem. If our efforts can be rewarded by promotion, so much the better, but at least we demand to be recognised for our efforts.

Conversely, long periods during which we receive little or no positive attention from our superiors makes us feel undervalued by the organisation and we retaliate by lowering our productivity. Why should we be interested in work, when they (the bosses) are not bothered about us?

If a person feels neglected in this way, then he will search for satisfaction elsewhere. Energy that should normally be consumed in legitimate activity at work will either be conserved for leisure time or diverted to challenge managerial authority, in an attempt to gain greater status in the eyes of his fellows. Whatever the outcome of frustrating his egoistical needs at work, the organisation will lose. Managers ignore this fact to their loss.

Psychological needs. The desire for personal growth and continuing development; to become knowledgeable and realise full potential.

Unfortunately for many people their employment has little to offer in the way of meeting these needs. The organisation of work into a series of almost meaningless tasks provides little scope for personal growth and the continuing acquisition of skills. Yet wherever it is possible for employees to undertake further training, widen their area of responsibility, exercise discretion, display initiative and allow those creative talents they possess to find expression at work, every opportunity should be grasped. For to satisfy his psychological needs, the highest he has, man will expend considerable energy. If these personal needs can be linked to organisational objectives, then the benefits accruing to both employer and employee will outweigh the effects of all other considerations.

An understanding of the influence of human needs on the bahaviour of people can be applied by a manager of a residential home to both the formulation of her objectives and the motivation of her staff. But simple awareness of the existence of hierarchial needs is in itself insufficient without an accompanying desire to base management techniques on their satisfaction.

Staff who feel adequately remunerated are unlikely to work harder if promised more money, for their wage has become secondary to other needs. The Home Manager who remarks 'My staff are well-paid, but they still won't co-operate' has become stuck at the physiological need level of motivation and is unlikely to make further progress.

Likewise the manager who sighs 'The staff are well-paid, it's almost impossible to sack them, yet I still hear them grumbling' has failed to recognise the importance of human needs beyond the security level. It is only by appreciating the power generated by all five levels of need, and utilising this resource to control the work of her care staff, that a manager can effectively deploy her staff and realise her objectives to improve the quality of life in her home.

There is no single managerial approach to staff motivation that will work for all Home Managers and all staff, in all situations, as circumstances, personalities and the urgency of objectives can change so much. The influence of human needs fluctuate also, but not in strength, only the level at which they are operational can vary from person to person. A more experienced member of staff may be searching for satisfaction of her physiological needs; a newer member for acceptance into the existing team - her social needs; yet a third, anxious that her husband has recently been made redundant, may feel the force of her security needs more consciously than others. The sensitive manager recognises not only the changing situation at work but the individual needs of her staff at particularly relevant stages in their personal life and development.

Successful staff management is then a function of a manager's attitude towards the needs of his staff and several theories have been advanced to reinforce this principle. Two of these theories are now examined in an attempt to glean additional knowledge for use in the management of homes.

Douglas M McGregor: *'The Human Side of Enterprise'*

The author postulates that management is faced with a choice between two distinct concepts when deciding the attitude it will adopt in approaching the fundamental problem of staff motivation. These two concepts he labels Theory X and Theory Y. In Theory X, which McGregor says is the conventional approach to staff management, he identifies three main principles which managers subscribe to:

1. Management is responsible for the control of money, materials, equipment and people in the economic interests of the organisation.

2. With respect to people this consists of directing their efforts, motivating them, controlling their actions and modifying their behaviour to fit the needs of the organisation.

3. Without this active intervention by management, people would be passive - even resistant - to organisational needs. They must therefore be persuaded, rewarded, punished to direct their activities. This is the job of managers.

To these *three* basic principles McGregor also adds *five* further beliefs which he says Theory X managers widely hold.

4. The average person is by nature indolent and works as little as possible.

5. He lacks ambition, dislikes responsibility and prefers to be led.

6. He is inherently self-centred and indifferent to organisational needs.

7. He is by nature resistant to change.

8. He is gullible, not very bright and readily duped.

Managers, says McGregor, have conceived a wide range of approaches to staff motivation, but they are all based on the foregoing assumptions. On the one hand there is a hard approach which places reliance on close supervision, tight controls over behaviour, coercion and disguised threats. On the other hand is a soft approach which attempts to direct behaviour by producing amenable conditions which will lull staff into accepting directions from management. This approach relies upon achieving harmony at work by satisfying demands and generally adopting a permissive atmosphere. Between these hard and soft extremes a variety of compromises have been explored - 'being firm, but fair' is a midway example.

McGregor comments that management has learned that Theory X produces difficulties however it is interpreted. Force leads to counter-force, restricts output by consuming energy that should be directed towards the benefit of the organisation and promotes militant unionism. Conversely the soft approach results in people taking advantage of the permissive attitude that was designed to woo them into accepting management objectives, causing them to expect more, but to give less, though otherwise being content. The compromise approach avoids the worst of either extremes but fails in itself to find a positive approach towards efficient management of staff.

McGregor admits that the last five points he makes about employees' attitude to work may indeed reflect accurately the current position. But he refutes strongly any suggestion that this is their natural state, saying people only behave in this way as an understandable response to the treatment they receive at work. Their attitude and behaviour is not a consequence of man's inherent nature, but a matter of measuring up to the perceived expectations of management. Perhaps the best way to indicate why this conventional approach to management is unsuccessful, suggests McGregor, is to examine the subject of motivation and he invites his readers to consider Maslow's hierarchy of human need.

If management is unable to stimulate its workforce to be more responsible in its attitude at work and increase production to acceptable rates, it should foster a more healthy respect for the influence of human needs. A management approach which concentrates on good wages, fringe benefits and steady employment as its incentives will quickly satisfy the physiological and safety needs of its employees. The staff will no longer be motivated by these basic needs and consequently their motivational emphasis will be moved to the social and egoistical levels. Unless suitable opportunities are then presented to permit the staff to satisfy these higher needs at work they will soon feel deprived and their deprivation will be reflected in their 'worsening' attitudes. People who are unable to find satisfaction for their higher needs during working hours will attempt to satisfy them outside the organisation. Because for many people this may be achieved in a limited way by the use of money, then they will demand higher wages (especially as management has made it clear it thinks this is all they are concerned with anyhow) thus reinforcing in the minds of the managers how correct their ideas on motivation are - a vicious circle!

Only for as long as management has the power to control the means of supplying man's physiological and safety needs can it force or bribe people to work effectively. The technique of threat and bribe - the 'carrot and stick' approach as McGregor defines it - can only work under circumstances where employees are struggling for subsistence and there are others willing to accept employment in their place. When employees start to be motivated primarily by their higher needs, the carrot and the stick technique fails simply because it is irrelevant to the situation. What is needed, says McGregor, is a new perspective on the management of staff that recognises in people the existence of higher needs, and exploits them to the mutual benefit of both staff and organisation. This new perspective McGregor calls Theory Y and in it suggests how the concepts of Theory X may be restyled.

1. Management is responsible for the control of money, materials, equipment and people in the interests of the organisation.

2. People are not by nature resistant to organisational needs or change, but become so only as a result of unhappy experiences at work.

3. Willingness to work, to accept responsibility, to develop skills are characteristics present in all people; management does not put them there. It is the duty of managers to encourage staff to recognise and develop their existing potentials.

4. It is the essential task of management to arrange work within the organisation so that the staff can satisfy their personal needs by directing their own efforts towards organisational objectives.

This process of creating opportunities, realising potential and encouraging growth, does not imply the abdication of management, the absence of leadership, the lowering of standards, or the other characteristics usually associated with the soft approach under Theory X. McGregor recognises that this new perspective is not without its difficulties for he says people today are accustomed to being directed, manipulated, controlled and being forced to seek satisfaction of their higher needs in their social life beyond work.

Frederick Herzberg: *Work and the Nature of Man*

Professor Herzberg attempted in his researches to discover those factors connected with an individual's work that gave rise to satisfying or dissatisfying experiences. His investigations lead to the formulation of his 'Motivation-Hygiene Theory'. Herzberg asked employees to note those incidents at work that led to extreme satisfaction and those that led to extreme dissatisfaction, on their part. Two main groupings emerged.

Those factors that contributed to job satisfaction were essentially concerned with the job itself - the job content, whereas those factors that resulted in job-dissatisfaction (Herzberg calls them dissatisfiers) were all part of the environment in which the work was performed - the job context.

Herzberg identifies five factors which he claims are strong determinants of job satisfaction: *they are achievement, recognition, work itself, responsibility and advancement.* The factors which are dissatisfiers, he recognises as *company policy and administration, supervision, salary, interpersonal relationships and working conditions.* (It is of interest to note at this point that the dissatisfiers correspond to Maslow's first three levels in his hierarchy and the satisfiers to the top two needs - egoistical and psychological needs.)

Herzberg terms the dissatisfiers Hygiene Factors because he claims they have nothing to do with the actual work, only the surroundings in which it is done, and any improvement to them results in less dissatisfaction with the job, but does not promote greater job satisfaction. The satisfier factors he terms at Motivator Factors, since the findings of his studies indicated that these factors were effective in stimulating the employees to superior performance and effort.

In essence the factors involved in producing job satisfaction are quite separate and distinct from those that lead to job satisfaction, and it is an important aspect of Herzberg's theory that these two groups of factors are not the opposite of each other.

The implication of Herzberg's 'Motivation-Hygiene Theory' is that any attempt by the management to improve such hygiene factors as working conditions, supervision, salary and administrative procedures will result only in the employees feeling less dissatisfied at work; it will not provide them with job satisfaction, increase their commitment to work or aid their efficiency and work output.

With reference here to Maslow's theory of man as a perpetually wanting creature, if regular increases to an employees wage are made he will temporarily feel his need for more money satiated, but will later expect a further increase in his remuneration or otherwise feel dissatisfaction. The automatic improvement in his pay will not necessarily motivate him to work harder, but develop in him the expectation of future rises without associated increase in work output. Likewise new office furniture, better canteen facilities and additional fringe benefits are all hygiene factors that in themselves contribute nothing to job satisfaction, but come to be regarded as a right in themselves.

Management, reasons Herzberg, must dwell on what people actually do at work, not just the conditions under which they perform their tasks. Because lack of motivating factors results in no job satisfaction, rather than in job dissatisfaction, their absence does not stimulate verbal complaints, as would the lack of hygiene factors, but it does produce apathy, with corresponding loss of interest and initiative. Unfortunately if management is unaware of the significance of these motivators in the work of its employees, then this disinterest in work, unwillingness to accept responsibility, or share in the urgency of organisational objectives is likely to be attributed to weaknesses in the employees' personality and their unsuitability for the job rather than to any fault of management in not motivating them properly. Yet it is impossible to show initiative if one is not granted the power of discretion, to accept responsibility if none is delegated or to be enthusiastic about one's job if it is too closely supervised or composed of a series of isolated tasks.

It would appear therefore that situations at work which people find most satisfying are those offering scope for achievement and recognition through the assumption of responsibility and the right to exercise discretion. Work situations which embrace these distinctive features are more than likely to succeed in motivating employees to strive effectively for organisational objectives. Conversely, work situations which fail to present such opportunities are prone to create frustration in the work force leading to ineffective production. In summary, managers who consider their staff by nature to be lazy, self-centred and unwilling to accept responsibility have a negative approach to management. They have failed to recognise the variety of incentives at their disposal. If governed by these false assumptions they attempt to motivate their staff by threats of disguised coercion they stand no chance of success and will fare little better by placing reliance on hygiene factors to gain co-operation through gratitude.

Although the research that leads to McGregor's and Herzberg's observations and conclusions was conducted in industrial situations there is no reason to suppose that their theories will not prove equally valid in the caring services. We have seen how staff respond in a positive or negative manner according to the way management attempts to motivate them, therefore it should be possible for managers of homes to adopt more appropriate management techniques in their own organisations.

A manager in a residential home for the elderly has perhaps an even more complex problem than her counterparts in industry. Her main objectives are not linked to profit and loss balance sheets, but to the health and happiness of her residents - products that do not lend themselves easily to quality control by her superiors at head office and for which she is seldom brought to account. If, however, she is to achieve the standards she has set for herself, she must consider her approach to staff motivation. The futility of relying on physiological/security needs alone has been made clear and the advantages of utilising social/egoistical/psychological needs stressed. But it is one thing agreeing with the ideas, quite another putting them into practice. What have current management theories to suggest in the way of practical methodology, and can they be adapted to routine in a residential home?

3.2 Job Enrichment

Even though a Manager of a Residential Home has responsibility for managing staff and for the quality of care provided, unless she/he is also the home owner it is likely that she has little or no control over such crucial factors as capital expenditure, conditions of employment, staff/resident ratios, or training budgets. It is as if she is given responsibility for a job but denied control over vital resources. In these circumstances it might seem that there is little power available to initiate the changes necessary to stimulate greater motivation of their staff. But if Herzberg's theory of job satisfaction residing in work itself, rather than the environment in which it is done, is accepted, there is then ample opportunity for Home Managers to motivate staff by redesigning the nature of their tasks thereby enriching the jobs they perform.

Several principles have been suggested for consideration before attempting to enrich a person's work and these principles can be examined with a view to the Manager adapting them to the work of the staff.

1. Give people whole jobs to do - natural units of work - so that they feel they can achieve something positive.

2. Remove the number of controls which staff are subjected to.

3. Give additional authority so that individuals have discretion in determining the way they are to achieve their objectives.

4. Increase the amount of information divulged to workers, so that they can see more of the complete picture.

5. Increase the accountability of people for their own jobs.

6. Introduce new and more demanding tasks not previously handled.

7. Give all individuals the opportunity to grow and develop their potential. [Reproduced from the **Industrial Society,** October 1968].

In general it would be unwise for a Home Manager to assume that all the staff would immediately react favourably to attempts at enriching their work. Enriched jobs are more involved, demand greater commitment - with a corresponding increase in energy expenditure - without any additional financial inducements. The benefits of greater job satisfaction that will follow are not immediately apparent and many staff may suspect that management is simply attempting to increase the amount of work they have to do for management's own good.

In a residential home the staff may resist proposed changes in the routine for exactly the same reason as residents themselves often resist changes on the grounds that 'we have always done it this way', suggesting an inviolate rule for precedent. Employees in institutions become institutionalised in the ways of the establishment by the same forces that act upon the residents and a Home Manager should prepare the ground with a well-considered scheme suitable for the Home before attempting to proceed with a job enrichment programme.

Preparation should begin by examining the current role of care staff within the home. Construct a list of the separate tasks which the staff perform, noting the time each task involves each week, and then arranging the tasks in descending order according to the time devoted to each one. If the care staff are asked to provide the information themselves, a more accurate picture may be obtained rather than one based on the Manager's own assessment. The following list of tasks has been devised from facts supplied by care staff attending a series of in-service training courses. Although the staff represented many different Residential Homes, little variation occurred in the nature of the tasks they said they performed or in the order in which they performed them:

Bedmaking
Table laying/clearing/food service
Dressing residents
Bathing residents
Toiletting residents
Tea rounds
Cleaning commodes
Laundry work
Checking/tidying of drawers and lockers

It is interesting to note that activities relating to the needs of the residents beyond their immediate bodily functions are omitted from the list. Resident contact appears to be incidental to the performance of other specific tasks, not a function in itself. This may be because staff are not actually encouraged to just sit and communicate with the residents or because they do not see such activity as an essential aspect of good residential care.

Having established the more time-consuming tasks of the care team, a next step for the Home Manager would be to compare these tasks with the objectives that have previously been formulated for the Home. If these objectives are similar to those itemised in 'Setting objectives', an immediate disparity between these objectives and the actual tasks of staff will be noted. This may be because the listed tasks are essential to the running of the Home and their performance requires such a disproportionate amount of time that other activities relating to the emotional needs of the residents are not done. Under these circumstances the Manager is apparently faced with two alternatives; either she can neglect some of the domestic features of her care assistants' work to re-direct their energies towards greater resident contact, or she can accept that since her staffing hours are inadequate her residents will not receive the degree of emotional stimulation she would like. Since any reduction in housekeeping tasks by her staff will be reflected in the physical standards of the Home, which will be more likely to attract criticism from visitors than the visual lethargy of her charges, she may be tempted to choose the second alternative. Such is the dilemma of the Home Manager. Her position could be relieved by an increase in staff hours but as this is unlikely she must seek a way out of her dilemma by other devices.

A programme of job enrichment itself may offer a solution, not by reducing the work load of the staff, but by heightening their commitment to the Home, improving their motivation and enhancing their efficiency. Care staff readily accept - certainly on training courses - that they are not grossly overworked but more frustrated by the system under which they are obliged to function; if this is so, then job enrichment may flourish.

In preparing her ground the manager should consider each of the seven principles of job enrichment previously listed and explore ways of applying them to the Home. As no two Residential Homes are the same, different managers will arrive at different applications, so the ideas developed below are for general guidance.

1. *Give people whole jobs to do - natural units of work - so that they feel they can achieve something positive.* Consider forming the care staff into small caring teams of two or three members, with each team having approximately the same number of weekly working hours (balancing full-time and part-time staff) and arrange their rotas so that at least one member of each team is on duty each day. Then divide the

residents into 'family groups' corresponding in number to the caring teams. Let each caring team understand that it is to be responsible for the physical and emotional welfare of its family group, through sharing in the activity programmes of the residents, by observing them closely and offering encouragement or assistance as required. This will enable the caring teams to be involved in far greater depth with fewer residents, covering the whole range of care. When new residents come into the home the appropriate teams will have to supervise their admission and participate in assessment and activity programming procedures.

Because residential care involves 24-hour attention and staff fall ill or have holidays, it will not always be practical for staff to relate to only one group of residents. But for the greater part it will be possible and, by keeping the teams and groups in small numbers, more intimate relationships will be formed and the staff can enjoy the benefits of having a natural unit of work, rather than constantly spreading their attention across the whole population of the home, dissipating their interest.

2. Remove the number of controls which staff are subjected to. Having informed each care team of the expectations you have of it, remove all unnecessary stipulations that constrain staff, preventing them displaying initiative and improving their own efficiency. Whilst you may expect each resident to have a bath at least weekly, allow the caring teams, in consultation with each person in their family group, to decide when. Similarly do not insist that residents be downstairs by 8.00am (or whatever time) for cooked breakfast, but make it known at what time breakfast will be served. Advise the staff that beds should be made before night-time, but refrain from stating an earlier, more definite time. In other words, reduce to a minimum the controls on the way in which the teams perform their duties, but introduce check systems to ensure abuse does not occur. You may wish, for example, to enquire weekly of the teams which of their residents missed a cooked breakfast, when baths were taken, and for specific details on the frailer residents.

3. Give additional authority so that individuals have discretion in determining the way they are to achieve their objectives. This principle complements the removal of controls from the task performance of the staff. Ceasing to stipulate the time residents are to rise in the mornings may cause insecurity in the minds of the staff who, although having previously grumbled at your regulations, knew precisely what to do and when. No longer having to perform a task at a given time may result in them continuing to do so simply because they have not considered alternatives.

Spell out to the staff in concise terms the areas over which they have your authority to exercise discretion in varying their work to meet the needs of the residents and their own routines. Make it clear that though you reserve the right to protect the interests of your residents for whom you have ultimate responsibility, you will respect their reasoning for the way they care for their groups within the broad limits you set. Place firmly upon the shoulders of the staff the responsibility for caring for their family groups, but stress it is incumbent upon them to know each resident thoroughly. Encourage them to meet on a professional level with social workers, doctors, religious representatives and homes inspectors wherever this will increase awareness of their residents. This delegation must, of course, be supported by the knowledge that the staff may turn to you or your deputies at any time for advice, guidance or support.

4. *Increase the amount of information divulged to workers.* Homes managers seek to keep vital details on residents to themselves and their deputies, refusing care staff access to case notes containing personal records of residents. The excuse advanced is the protection of confidentiality but the real reason is often the reinforcement of the position of the Home's manager as the fount of all information, permitting her to say. 'I know best' without fear of contradiction.

Care staff cannot be expected to assume wider briefs, accept responsibility and exercise discretion if necessary information is withheld. Until a Manager is more certain of her staff she can elect to provide condensed notes which leave out sensitive details for general distribution to the caring teams, or she can discuss verbally the case notes with the staff to obviate the need for the staff to read them in detail. Increasing the amount of information distributed also implies taking the staff into her confidence about the wider aspects of the home; providing them with facts about such legitimate interests as new admissions, reports made by inspection officers and the occupancy levels necessary for the Home to financially break even. Unless there are specific contra-indications there is nothing that needs to be confidential about this type of information and divulging it will do much to enhance staff identification with the Home and its progress.

5. *Increase the accountability of people for their own jobs.* Delegation of accountability is a management skills difficult to operate for it involves managers in defining their objectives clearly, briefing staff fully, relaxing controls, being less involved in detail and sitting out of the limelight whilst their staff work. Some managers are reluctant to do this for they either like the idea of staff constantly referring to them or their insecurity makes them fearful of junior staff appearing too competent. But without staff being responsible for their own spheres of work, answerable for the consequences of their actions and being praised or blamed accordingly, a job-enrichment programme becomes meaningless.

Making people accountable for their areas of work should not be confused with senior staff abdicating their role as managers. Indeed their own jobs increase in complexity for they must retain ultimate responsibility for their organisation; selecting, training, encouraging and checking their staff thoroughly so that no one member is given responsibility beyond her preparation and capacity.

In a residential home with a family group system the caring team will have more loosely defined work, access to additional information, authority to exercise discretion and greater freedom from immediate supervision. To this must be added accountability for their actions at agreed checkpoints. If a Home Manager cannot bring herself to give responsibility to staff and hold them accountable for the care of the residents she will feel the need to constantly interfere, insisting that tasks are carried out by her methods, in her place, at her time. The effect will completely negate any attempt at job-enrichment. If one accepted objective for the home, and therefore the caring team, is to stimulate the residents' involvement in recreational activities, then for the provision of the necessary facilities and giving encouragement the staff ought to be held accountable, but not for when and where; this must be left to their own discretion based upon a closer understanding of their residents and the dictates of other tasks. However they must be prepared to justify to management the reasons for whatever they do or do not provide. The same reasoning applies to all other objectives.

6. *Introduce new and more demanding jobs.* Many of the duties performed by the care staff will be of a routine yet essential nature, and though responsibility for organising their own work loads will enrich their jobs, the programme can be much enhanced by the addition of more demanding work at suitable opportunities present themselves. From the original list detailing the separate tasks undertaken by the care assistants there will probably be absent many notable aspects of the Home's activities, for example visiting new residents prior to admission, accompanying doctors during visits to residents, contacting relatives, visiting residents in hospital - activities normally the preserve of a Manager or her deputies. As the care staff increase in confidence and capability it should become possible to select from these additional tasks ones that can, with further training and guidance, be handed over to care staff on an increasing number of occasions. All the time that can be saved will be needed to meet the demands of the new role as a true manager.

7. *Give all individuals the opportunity to grow and develop.* A programme of job enrichment will in itself cause staff to grow in professional stature at work and realise more of their latent potential. It will also stimulate individuals to seek even greater responsibility and to question the principles underlying the provision of residential care.

To this end all staff should be encouraged to participate in the National Vocational Qualifications (NVQ) system of awards, which is ideally suited to the needs of residential care staff. NVQ training enables individuals, whilst in work and at their own pace, to develop clearly prescribed and nationally recognised practical competences. NVQ training not only develops the work skills of staff but, like all successful training, increases their self-worth, makes them feel valued by management, and improves morale.

A detailed explanation of NVQ and their application to residential care is given in Chapter 6.

One effect of encouraging individuals to develop their potential and acquire recognised qualification may be that some of the staff will leave the Home for promotion elsewhere. This will be inevitable, but the benefits will already have been experienced from their increasing contributions.

A job enrichment programme cannot be implemented by an overnight edict. For reasons mentioned previously, the staff may initially suspect motives and show resistance to the changes proposed. These reactions may be lessened by carefully explaining to all employees why the scheme should be implemented, discussing whatever consequences are envisaged and taking pains to explain that although the new approach may increase each person's job satisfaction, it will involve more varied and demanding work all round. Having introduced this concept to the staff sufficient time should elapse to allow the staff to reflect upon the implications themselves and air their thoughts. (They may even suggest possible ways of improving the model). Only when the staff have had enough time to mull over the proposals should they be implemented. Unless there is substantial opposition to the scheme it should be followed through with problems being ironed out as they arise, and reluctant staff being brought in gradually. The residents themselves will be affected, hopefully for the better, and their co-operation will be essential. It will have to be decided whether they will understand an explanation of the working of a family grouped organisation better from the Manager or from their care team members.

The above is only an outline suggestion for job-enrichment programmes. Finer details will require further consideration by individual managers according to the nature of their own Homes. Many difficulties may not be predictable, arising only after the adoption of a scheme, but one result of the proposed change should be to foster greater team work amongst all grades of staff and given this benefit no problem should be insurmountable.

The more cautious manager may wish, at first, only to proceed with minor changes, awaiting practical evidence of success, before attempting to implement a more advanced programme.

CHAPTER 4
Managing the Home

At selection interviews for management positions, candidates are sometimes asked what qualities they feel a successful leader possesses. The typical response of candidates to this question is to list a series of seemingly appropriate qualities, as examples come to mind.

A sense of humour

Above average intelligence

Technical competence

Sense of justice

Capacity to accept responsibility

Imagination

Willingness to delegate

Good health

Energy

Integrity

Freedom from prejudices

4.1 Leadership & what it is

Candidates who reply with answers as above are then faced with a dilemma when asked to say whether they feel these qualities are developed in themselves. For if they say 'yes', the panel is likely to doubt their capacity for self-analysis, and, if they reply 'no', they place themselves in the embarrassing position of having to identify personal failings. What purpose this exercise serves is difficult to assess, since successful leadership revolves round much more than the possession of a string of virtues. Indeed, as J A C Brown points out in his book *The Social Psychology of Industry* - some of the most successful leaders in history have been neurotic, insane, epileptic, humourless, narrow-minded, unjust and authoritarian; there have been religious leaders with a pathological sense of guilt, political leaders with delusions of omnipotence, and military leaders with delusions of persecution. Yet such individuals in their own fields, in their own periods, have been most effective leaders. Effective leadership is therefore a most complex topic which cannot be approached by a simple analysis of the qualities possessed by its successful exponents. In searching for an answer to the intriguing question 'What is it that enables some people to lead and causes others to follow?', we can begin by examining the nature of leadership power. The act of leadership is inseparable from the use of power and authority, since all leaders must give instructions, expect them to be obeyed and threaten sanctions if they are not, and the sources of leadership power vary.

1. *Traditional source*. Down the ages subjects have repeatedly granted their kings the right to exercise control over them until the power positions of kings has become established by tradition. A hereditary source.

2. *Democratic source*. Prime ministers, chairmen of committees and presidents of societies are elected to power positions. During their term of office, within prescribed terms of reference, their dictates are followed. However because their authority stems from the will of the majority they can be removed from office at anytime.

3. *Sapiential source*. The specialist knowledge or technical skills of certain individuals are recognised by others, and in circumstances relevant to their qualifications the authority of these individuals is accepted. Sapiential authority may be of a more lasting nature, as in the case of doctors and their patients, or transient, as when in a crisis obvious technical expertise, or valuable personal qualities, mark out an individual for group leadership. Then, as long as the crisis persists, group members will accept the leader's authority.

4. Charismatic source. By sheer force of personality, leaders develop considerable hold over their followers, and the motion generated by their presence causes their followers to reinforce each other's acceptance of their leader's position. In such situations the leader's power becomes unquestioned, almost unlimited, and may even grow after death.

5. *Forced source*. Men with guns, for example, can seize power over those without guns. Their position is the reverse of charismatic leadership, and they are reluctantly obeyed, simply because of the consequence they threaten. However as long as they remain the only ones with guns they can persist as leaders.

6. *Bureaucratic source*. In bureaucratic organisations power and authority appears to reside in an individual occupying the highest position in a hierarchial structure. It then flows downwards, by the

process of delegation, through an ever-widening network of subordinates. The authority of each individual comes directly from the position he holds to which he has been formally appointed. By paying wages, offering chances for greater power, and threatening internal sanctions, bureaucracies protect their own power system. Armed forces, industrial organisations and social services departments are examples of bureaucratic organisations.

A central feature of leadership (or 'followship') is therefore the origin and nature of the leader's power or authority. In residential homes - bureaucratic organisations - the management of people is very much dependent upon the use of power and authority and its effect upon others.

The terms 'power' and 'authority' however, are not synonyms, and each concept has significant implications for all managers. In bureaucratic organisations managers have authority over subordinates which has been delegated to them by their superiors. The authority stems from the formal positions they hold and is not a product of their personality. Its exercise is only legitimate as long as it is restricted to the formal work of the organisation. Power, on the other hand, has no legitimate basis in bureaucracies, but arises as a by-product of a position held. It is nevertheless a most potent influence and its abuse can be a cause for much concern.

The manager's secretary, for instance, may use her position to expedite or delay appointments to see her boss for her own personal reasons, or managers may overlook merit of staff to promote personal favourites. In residential homes cooks and care staff may organise routines to suit themselves rather than residents.

Generally, positional power is used for self-interest and its abuse must be guarded against.

Why subordinates in a bureaucracy should choose to accept rather than reject the authority of their superiors is an important consideration for all managers, since their personal careers and the success of their organisation depends upon them obtaining this compliance. An individual employee may have one or more reasons for accepting the authority of his superiors.

1. He may be attracted by the rewards consequent upon his acceptance - maintaining employment, increased pay, praise or promotion.

2. He may fear the formal sanctions that would follow if he refused to comply.

3. He may have been socialised into a behavioural pattern that requires him to accept legitimate authority.

4. He may anticipate the criticism of his colleagues should he reject the system.

5. He may identify strongly with the aims of the organisation and recognise that his acceptance of authority facilitates their attainment.

6. He may simply prefer to follow instructions rather than make decisions himself.

7. He may respond to the personal qualities of a superior whom he admires.

Not all people accept the formal authority structure of bureaucracy, and may rebel. This they may do in isolation from others, or as members of activated groups. However because of the legitimacy of the position of bureaucracies and their control over resources, bureaucracies generally manage to preserve their authority. Individual rebels are sooner or later forced to comply or leave the organisation and rebellious groups - who may enjoy considerable temporary power - persist only until their members' grievances or aspirations have been resolved. For the most part individuals are prepared to accept the use of legitimate bureaucratic authority. But it is worth noting that happy, satisfied workers do not respond automatically to the exhortations of agitators. No matter how persuasive a speaker, he can only exploit potential unrest by appealing to *existing* frustrations in his co-workers.

A manager's use of legitimate authority in a bureaucracy is limited to his formal role in the organisation. Furthermore, because he is constrained by the objectives of his organisation, the dictates of his superiors, union agreements and national laws he is not free to lead his staff in the manner that group leaders outside bureaucracies and without regulations are able to lead their followers. A manager's talents and personality have often to be moulded to reflect the philosophies of his organisation, and his capacity to act spontaneously in encouraging others to follow him, is correspondingly curtailed. It is not his true role to offer inspired leadership, capitalising on magnetic personal qualities, to lead followers towards an end only he can visualise but more to co-ordinate the work of his staff to achieve recognised and shared objectives. Viewed in this light the words 'leader' and 'leadership qualities' are perhaps not the most appropriate terms when considering the work of a manager of a home - 'manager' and ' management styles' are more relevant expressions.

4.2 Management styles

Successful management is a product of an interaction between the manager, the managed and the situation in which they work. It is not a factor of the manager's personality alone, but his technique in controlling himself, his staff and his environment. Given this premise any officer-in-charge of a home can improve her management technique by conscious thought and practice. This process she can begin by considering some of the various management styles that have been classified, and discovering which style most closely approximates to her own. Having done this she can then compare the relative values of the various styles and try to adapt her own towards one considered more likely to lead to greater success. Since the basic principles of management are common to all bureaucracies, the fact that these styles are couched in industrial terms should not detract from their value to a manager of a residential home.

McGregor's theory X and theory Y approaches to management with their diametrically opposed philosophies were looked at in Chapter 3 when motivation was examined. Two other authorities are now considered.

J A C Brown - *The Social Psychology of Industry*

Brown divides managerial styles into the three traditional groups:

1. *Autocratic:* a. Strict Autocrat; b. Benevolent Autocrat, c. Incompetent Autocrat

2. *Democratic:* a. Genuine Democrat, b. Pseudo Democrat

3. *Laissez-faire*

1. *Autocratic.* In this classification autocratic managers are characterised by their self-centres approach to management. They give clear, concise orders with the expectation of them being obeyed without question. In their philosophy the good of the organisation always comes first and they willingly pour their considerable energy into work, expecting others to do the same. They recognise no need to consult their subordinates because they consider it valueless, as no one knows better than themselves. In their personal relationships with staff they keep themselves somewhat as a psychological distance, discouraging familiarity and retreating more into the sanctity of their superior position whenever situations become difficult.

The Strict Autocrat is generally technically competent, drives his staff hard, is unscrupulous in his dealings and bends rules if it facilitates the attainment of his objectives. As a manager he is disliked both by his subordinates and his superiors, though he is respected for his capacity to 'get things done' and his willingness to accept responsibility. For his part he gives respect to his own bosses, if only for the position they hold, and is fair to his staff, particularly those he considers loyal. He is not particularly concerned about his own popularity.

The Benevolent Autocrat is similarly orientated towards results and the good of his organisation. He too issues his orders, demands compliance, works hard at his job and expects others to do the same. However some of his energies are directed towards the welfare of his staff, but because his concern is clouded by what he thinks is good for them, not what they want, his interference is resented and his advice often rejected. He would like to be liked by his staff, as opposed to the Strict Autocrat who is not bothered about their feelings towards him.

The Incompetent Autocrat aspires to be all powerful and mimics the Strict Autocrat's approach. Although he has energy he lacks technical competence; this failing, combined with his inability to motivate staff, makes him uncertain how to reach his objectives. Basically he is an insecure person who, to protect his own image, subconsciously surrounds himself with even less competent workers and then complains bitterly that he has no one to rely upon to get anything done.

2. *Democratic.* The Genuine Democrat sees his role as co-ordinating the activities of a working team. While technically competent in his field he recognises that his juniors have much to offer and encourages them to contribute ideas. His motive in doing so is not to arrive as a compromise opinion, but to obtain all available information necessary for him to make the most appropriate decision. The Genuine Democrat recognises that in the longer term his organisation will prosper more if it is served by staff whose talents have been fully extended. He subscribes to the view that all his staff have, to a greater or lesser degree, potential for growth and he delegates work according to individual capacities, encouraging staff to accept greater responsibilities and training them in the appropriate skills. He promotes people purely on merit. The Genuine Democrat works hard at his management task and prides himself on the fact that things will run smoothly in his absence. His quiet, confident approach gains both results and respect.

The Pseudo-Democrat on the other hand attempts to imitate the Genuine Democrat but does not possess the necessary skills. Because he lacks the capacity to select and train staff properly and delegate effectively he constantly feels the need to interfere. His wish to be popular and his need to make appropriate managerial decisions often conflict. The result is a compromise between his own choice and the wishes of his staff which produces confusion and limits production. The Pseudo-Democrat is as ineffective as the Incompetent Autocrat, differing only in his approach to staff relationships.

3. *Laissez-faire.* The Laissez-faire manager generally opts out of his responsibilities, setting vague objectives for his subordinates and then leaving them to cope as best they can. He interferes as little as possible in the work of his staff, either to praise or constructively criticise. Being content to sit on the side lines, abdicating his managerial functions, he allows an enterprising individual to seize power for himself, irrespective of his abilities. Under these circumstances the staff flounder and productivity is low.

With the autocratic approach (excepting the incompetent) the sheer drive and momentum generated by the hyperactive manager produces results, and in time of crisis or uncertainty there is a considerable degree of comfort to be gained from being controlled by a person who knows where to go and how to get there. When decisions have to be taken quickly there is little to be gained by a technically competent manager consulting with subordinates who probably know less. However, in the longer term, when the crisis has passed and conditions are more stable, the continuation of an autocratic style creates resentment, causes reduced efficiency, and leads to absenteeism or resignations. Those staff who remain with the organisation are the least able and even they fail to realise their potential. Frustration reigns and the rating for dissatisfaction at work is high. The strength of the autocratic style lies in the manager himself, and when he is not present productivity falls dramatically.

The democratic style (excepting the pseudo-democrat) is more appropriate in conditions where the organisations is efficient and stable. In these circumstances a democratic approach fosters a continuing spirit of co-operation, with high morale, and employees identifying personally with the objectives of the organisation. Potential is realised and a work pattern is established that does not revolve round the presence of the manager. Discipline exists in a democratic environment, perhaps more strongly than it does in an autocratic one, since it is internally developed rather than externally imposed. The manager does not sacrifice his authority when he consults with his staff, in fact his position is strengthened because he carries the group with him.

With the laissez-faire style the degree of confusion produced depends upon the skills and maturity of the team members. In small groups where each person is well-qualified in his field and internally motivated by interest in his work, the system may continue for some time. It is in moments of crisis, or when drastic policy changes are required, that the deficiencies become glaringly apparent.

R R Blake and J S Mouton - *The Managerial Grid*

Blake and Mouton have provided a basis for conveniently classifying the attitudes and behaviour of managers at work - that is their style or approach to the management task. They have devised a graph, or Grid , having rectangular axes each divided into nine sections, as shown in the diagram, with the vertical axes representing 'concern for people' and the horizontal axes representing 'concern for production'.

In devising this Managerial Grid, Blake and Mouton reasoned that a manager has two main areas of concern - people and production. He has the dual concern for the people in his organisation, his subordinates, colleagues and bosses, and for production of goods or the provision of services. In this dichotomy how he divides his energies or where he places his emphasis can be plotted on the managerial grid to graphically reveal his style.

Thus a manager who has high concern for productivity, 8 or 9 on the horizontal axes, but who gives little consideration to his staff, 1 or 2 on the vertical axes, would appear in the bottom right hand corner of the Grid. Conversely an individual who concentrates his attention primarily on the happiness of his staff, 8 or 9 on the vertical axes, but who has little concern for production, 1 or 2 on the horizontal axes, would be positioned in the top left hand corner of the Grid. Therefore any manager's position on the Blake and Mouton Grid can be described by two numbers, with the vertical axes number quoted first, eg, 9,1.

THE MANAGERIAL GRID

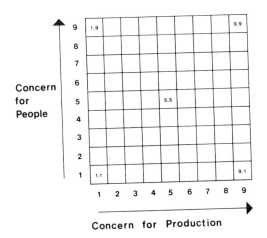

47

A total of 81 positions are possible on the Grid but the managerial styles of managers who occupy the four corners and the centre of the Grid are the ones most commonly selected for detailed description.

Thus managers around the *1,1 corner* of the Grid opt out of the managerial situation - completely abdicating their responsibilities. They generate nothing new and rely upon their subordinates to provide what little momentum that exists. When 1,1-oriented managers are faced with differences of opinion amongst their subordinates they manoeuvre away from the situation leaving their staff to settle matters as best they might. Such managers do as little work as possible commensurate with remaining in office and have no greater expectation from their staff. Their sense of humour is often inappropriate to the situation.

The *1,9-oriented managers,* however, are not so neutral to events around them. They place emphasis on maintaining good staff relationships and strive to create a harmonious environment by going along with the suggestions of their staff. The 1,9-oriented managers offer to help their staff, but seldom lead, and when conflict arises their energies go into defusing the situation at the expense of gaining something creative. Their sense of humour is employed to divert pressure away from the origin of the conflict to ease the tension.

Diametrically opposed to the 1,9-oriented individuals on the Grid are the *9,1-oriented* managers whose accent is very much on task performance irrespective of the feeling of their staff. They work hard and expect their subordinates to do the same, but with little or no personal discretion. As managers they frequently insist that their way is the best and only way, and when confronted they use their positional authority to counter opposition. They pride themselves on their hard approach and there is an element of sarcasm in their humour.

The centre of the Grid is occupied by the *5,5-oriented managers* - the compromisers - who divide their energies between getting the job done and keeping their subordinates happy. Though capable of generating their own ideas they are prepared to moderate their decisions to accommodate the opinions of their staff. When faced with differences of opinion they seek a compromise solution to placate the opposition even though this may involve some sacrifice of task performance. They are orientated towards fairness, though as compromisers when under pressure they are often uncertain of the best angle to take to reduce tension. Under these circumstances 5,5-oriented managers may use their sense of humour to advantage.

The *9,9-oriented* managers have high concern for both their task performance and the people they work with. Although confident of their own abilities they encourage their subordinates to contribute ideas and are prepared to moderate their initial thoughts in the light of sound advice, even from juniors. 9,9-oriented managers are dynamic, hard-working, but considerate managers who by stimulating their staff to participate actively fully gain optimum mature co-operation. When differences of opinion arise they question, listen and attempt to understand why, using the dialogue to advantage. They may not remain unemotional in such discussions but they control themselves without displays of anger and their sense of humour is always appropriate and puts matters into perspective.

The Managerial Grid is designed not simply to label managers but to assist them in the identification of their current approach as part of a comprehensive training scheme that aims to encourage them to adopt a more appropriate managerial style. The implication of the Blake and Mouton theory being that the closer a manager is to the 9,9 pattern the more effective he will be as a manager.

Relating this to the previous classification, the Blake and Mouton 9,9 position corresponds to the Genuine Democrat, the 1,1 position to the Laissez-faire manager, and the 9,1 position to the Strict Autocrat. The 5,5 manager is a compromiser who seeks a balance between acceptable production levels and harmonious human relations, whereas the 1,9 manager places his emphasis entirely upon the avoidance of conflict by demanding the minimum amount and creating a peaceful environment.

In addition to the theories of managerial styles touched upon so far, there are the models of F E Fielder - A *Theory of Leadership Effectiveness;* W J Reddin - *Managerial Effectiveness* and Rensis Likert - *The Human Organisation,* plus several other authorities.

In the confusion of theories available the new student of managerial principles can be forgiven for wondering which, if any, is the most appropriate style to adopt. However the absence of a single clearly acknowledged model for managerial effectiveness (and it is doubtful if one will ever arise*) does not diminish the value of their study. Their worth lies not in the offer of an ideal style of management to be blindly copied, but in providing standards against which an individual may compare his or her own performance and question that approach. In this respect an exercise in critical self-analysis can be of equal value to the manager of a residential home as it is to managers in other situations. Classical examples of autocrats, democrats, compromisers and laissez-faire managers are to be found in residential homes with no less frequency than in other bureaucratic organisations and between these examples range a whole spectrum of other styles that would fill Blake's grid.

Many a Home is run by an Incompetent Autocrat who struts through her province, issuing orders, making decisions, getting things done; a person who has no doubt of her own ability and who is constantly plucking from a bank of superficial quotations a phrase to deal with any situation. With an authoritarian, even bullying approach, the Home is organised with military efficiency and Autocrat dominates in every field, calling upon years of experience to justify her actions and to pour scorn on newfangled ideas.

With an emphasis on disinfectant, hospital beds and regular routine the Autocrat moulds the residents to fit the Home, rather than arranges the establishment to meet their needs. Such a Manager is dangerous, for her objectives are misplaced and her ideas on motivation inappropriate. To maintain her position in the face of dissent she increasingly relies on her autocratic approach. As a result the spirited residents become cowed and her better staff leave, and although the management committee may be troubled little by the Home (as far as complaints are relevant) they recognise its poor standards of care.

Examples of laissez-faire management are shown by those Managers who hide behind artificial mountains of paperwork that serve as an effective excuse for remaining officebound. Their lack of contact with residents and staff leaves them oblivious to their respective needs and the staff follow a basic routine inherited from previous workers and perpetuated if for no better reason than 'it's always been done like this'. When change in routine does occur it is based on ill-founded compassion by the staff, or the dictates of their personal convenience. With the staff left to their own devices this type of management causes the Home to deteriorate to a point where intervention by senior officials is required or, given a capable staff, a low but passable standard is maintained.

Managers of Homes who seek a compromise whenever conflict arises between meeting the needs of the residents and suiting the convenience of staff or administrative expedience - Blake and Mouton 5,5 managers - also abound in the Homes. These Heads sacrifice some caring standards in the supposed interest of harmonious staff relations, and, although their Homes never attract criticism, they fail to attain the higher standards possible.

Each managerial approach ever described has some adherents in Residential Homes - which may help to explain the diversity in caring standards. If this is so, then considerable scope for improvement lies in a Home Manager increasing her knowledge of the various models of managerial effectiveness. This knowledge can enhance self-awareness, assist critical assessment and promote practical development of improved techniques. A Home Manager who is aware of the different styles, with their known pitfalls and merits, is in a far better position to adopt a more successful approach to the management of her staff than one who has only her personal experience to call upon and nothing to compare it with.

4.3 DELEGATION

Managers frequently complain of the demanding nature of their positions. Not only are they charged with responsibility for the special needs
of elderly residents 24 hours a day, but they must also attend to other
duties which are central to the smooth running of a Home. There are
staff vacancies to be filled, rotas arranged, absences covered; new
residents admitted; letters written, telephones answered; food ordered,
bills paid, returns completed; visitors received; the home's fabric maintained; plus a host of peripheral activities that seem to arise indiscrimi-
nantly. Add to these responsibilities the necessity of communicating
with headquarters or owners difficult to contact, a public quick to
criticise, announced and unannounced inspections -- and it is not
surprising that a Manager feels overwhelmed, especially if she attempts
to attend to everything herself.

But closer inspection of what she does often reveals her to be spending
hours doing tasks that could easily be handled by members of her staff,
if only she would delegate the responsibility. That the staff have the
capacity and desire to accept increasing responsibility within the homes
we discussed in Chapter 3 when we examined staff motivation and the
suggested seven principles for the introduction of a job-enrichment
programme.

To implement these principles requires considerable skill in delegation,
and it is a skill that many managers unfortunately fail to develop. Proper
delegation not only enriches the work of the staff, but reduces the
burden of routine activities on the manager; its advantages are enor-
mous. Yet despite these advantages many managers fail to exploit the
value of delegation, either because they do not properly understand
what it is or, in their ignorance, they fear its effects.

Delegation is a process of allocating recognisable elements of an
organisation's work to a junior, with the accompanying authority to
function under his own discretion and accountability for the consequence of his actions. The process of delegation should not be confused with the action of 'giving out work'. In delegation the junior is given
long term results to achieve, has freedom to plan his own methods, to
take decisions and use agreed resources. Because his work is monitored only at agreed checkpoints he has freedom of action and may do
things quite differently from his boss. On the other hand, when a junior
is 'given work' he is told what to do, how to do it and when; his activities
are placed under close supervision and he has little or no freedom to
'do his own thing'.

It is important at this stage to distinguish also between delegation, pseudo-delegation and abdication. The true delegator allocates work according to an individual's ability, gives the necessary authority, remains accessible for advice and monitors his junior's progress at previously agreed checkpoints. When the true delegator discovers errors he uses the occasions as training sessions to improve the skill of his junior.

The pseudo-delegator similarly allocates complete areas of work, but because he is unsure of his own position or frightened in case he is 'dropped in it' he constantly interferes. When he discovers a potential difficulty he takes over himself or insists the work is done his way, so his juniors are denied all chances to develop.

The abdicator, on the other hand, hives off work - particularly that which he does not like doing himself - to poorly briefed, inadequately trained staff, leaving them to cope with work beyond their capacities. He fails to agree occasions for performance checks and only intrudes when things have gone wrong, and it is too late for correction.

The answer then to the complaints of the over-worked Home Manager is to delegate more work - more effectively. The advantages of delegation to the manager are that it:

a. Reduces routine work.

b. Frees her to concentrate on the greater needs of her home.

c. Makes the introduction of a job-enrichment programme possible - increasing staff commitment and motivation.

d. Utilises to the full the pool of staff skills.

e. Increases the skills of individual staff by developing their potential.

f.   Strengthens teamwork.

g. Adds to her personal job-satisfaction by witnessing the development of her staff and the improved welfare of her residents.

Although the advantages of delegating work to subordinates are very real, many Managers fail to delegate for a variety of reasons:

They feel that as they are accountable for running of the home they must undertake all responsible work themselves.

They believe it is quicker and easier to continue attempting all tasks themselves.

They are reluctant to relinquish immediate control of any aspect of the Home's organisation.

They wish to receive direct credit for all 'progress' made.

They feel secure by being busy and see constant observable activity as justification of their position.

They feel no one could possibly do the job as well as themselves.

They feel frightened in case they are 'dropped in it'.

They feel threatened by the possibility of staff proving more competent than themselves.

They suspect the ability of their staff to maintain confidentiality.

They feel constrained by their staff job-description.

They have tried delegating once and it failed.

None of the above are adequate reasons for refusing to delegate work, they are simply personal excuses and reflect the whole approach of a manager to her management task. The fear of things going wrong if she delegates work is an obvious deterrent, but it is a fear that can be lessened by anticipating difficulties and taking sensible precautions. Possible causes of failure which can be avoided are:

The work areas delegated and the capacity of the juniors not being matched, resulting in staff having responsibility beyond their ability.

Otherwise capable members of staff not thoroughly understanding their responsibilities through inadequate briefings.

Subordinates not properly appreciating the consequences of their actions.

The absence of agreed checkpoints where the Home Manager can monitor the work of her subordinates.

The Home Manager not being readily available for advice and information.

The Home Manager constantly interfering once the work has been delegated, so that the subordinates do not know the full extent of their responsibilities.

A change in emphasis, away from centralised responsibility towards a wider acceptance, is a project demanding considerable planning, the first stages of which involve the choice of work areas to be delegated. This can be accomplished by the homes manager listing all the major aspects of her current work and then highlighting those self-contained areas that are suitable to be delegated, bearing in mind the degree of delegation she is initially attempting.

The second stage is to analyse the capacity of individual staff to accept increased responsibility. This the Home Manager can do by asking herself a series of questions about each member of staff she has in mind. Seven questions which are usually applicable are the following:

1. What are his/her qualifications, skills and experience?

2. Which of these are being used now?

3. Which are not being used?

4. Can the individual be trained for additional tasks?

5. What are his/her obvious limitations?

6. What aspects of the work of the home does the person particularly like and dislike?

7. What are the individual's views on accepting greater responsibilities in the Home?

The third stage is to match the proposed areas of work to be delegated with the profile of the staff to be involved in the programme of increased delegation. An ideal relationship between the two may not immediately be apparent, in which case the homes manager will either have to modify the work areas by removing certain components, or initiating training exercises to develop the skills necessary to enable staff to undertake the unmodified tasks. A combination of these two courses is quite practical, and the action taken by the Manager will depend upon her assessment of the situation. Once the work areas and staff have been matched, the fourth stage is to brief each individual in detail concerning the new responsibilities so that each fully understands:

1. The personal area of responsibility

2. The consequence of the carer's actions

3. All relevant information or where to obtain it.

4. The limits of the carer's discretion

5. The importance of seeking advice

6. The points at which the carer's work will be monitored

7. When to assume the extra responsibility

Whether the Home Manager is simply considering delegating a specific aspect of the Home's routine - for example, responsibility for the assessment of residents - to a deputy or planning a programme of job-enrichment for her care assistants, thorough planning is the active ingredient of success.

A Manager would be advised not to restrict her attentions to the caring staff, all grades of employees in the homes have potential to accept wider responsibilities.

4.4 Communications

In all bureaucratic organisations from time to time communications break down; information fails to reach its intended destination, becomes distorted in transmission or never actually leaves its source:

'No one told us she was being admitted today.'

'He says he asked Deputy to remind his mother he wouldn't be visiting last week, Deputy was off and no one else knew - and his mother was very upset.'

When communications break down like this in organisations caring for the frail elderly, the consequences are exceedingly harmful and the communications system comes under heavy criticism. It is said that a better system is needed, then such things would not happen. Yet it is seldom a fault of the system that causes communications to break down; invariably human error is to blame. Because of the involvement of people in communications, no system can be perfected, though efficiency can be improved and errors reduced by a clearer under-standing of how communication systems work.

At least two people are involved with a communication - the *originator* who has the initial thoughts (or message) to transfer and the *recipient* to whom they are directed. To transfer these thoughts from one to another requires a *transmission* system (See Figure 4.a) The systems commonly employed for internal communications are:

* face to face conversation

* telephone conversation

* memo to be collected/delivered

* verbal message via a third party

Since any system, other than telepathy, cannot transmit thoughts the originator must *encode* his thoughts into signals before transmission through the system and the recipient must *decode* the same signals after transmission back into thoughts (see Figure 4.b).

Figure 4.a

ORIGINATOR	TRANSMISSION SYSTEM	RECIPIENT

Figure 4.b

ORIGINATOR --- ENCODES SIGNALS --- TRANSMISSION SYSTEM --- DECODES SIGNALS --- RECIPIENT

This is a simplified model of a communications system for the passage of thoughts (messages) from one individual to another, but its simplicity is useful in that it helps to identify the stages at which communications are most likely to fail, and from this knowledge appropriate precautions can be taken to minimise errors. It is vital to realise that no communication has been effected until the recipient has received and decoded the originator's thoughts, for many errors are made by people being content to initiate a communication without taking adequate steps to ensure it will be received.

A Manager can put this communications model to good use by considering the various stages involved before she attempts to communicate.

Initial Thoughts. Clarity of thought is the essence of good communications. If the originator is unsure of what to communicate then no system will compensate this deficiency, more than likely it will compound the confusion.

The transmission system. *Face-to-face communication* is the transmission system least prone to mistakes. It reduces the time and distance between transmissions and reception and permits questions to be asked quickly to check understanding. The originator knows instantly the communication has been received. It can, however, be time consuming and certainly is not practical on every occasion.

Telephone conversations have many of the benefits of face to face conversations and distance is no problem. However this system has certain disadvantages

1. The benefits of body language are lost; a frown or a shrug which in face to face conversations would indicate lack of understanding are not to be seen.

2. The originator cannot determine whether the recipient is paying attention or is being distracted by other events - a third party presence, paperwork etc.

3. The originator cannot detect if a private communication is being overheard.

4. Not all wanted recipients are available by phone.

A *memo system* used when direct conversation is not possible provides a permanent record that can be re-read as required, but it has serious drawback caused by:

1. The time lapse between initiating a communication and its recipient.

2. Establishing an efficient system for the collection or delivery of memos.

3. The originator's uncertainty about the recipients receipt of a memo.

4. The ambiguity of certain words and phrases.

A *third party system* employed to transmit a verbal message is not without its attendant problems either, but these can be identified by specific questions.

1. Does the messenger know how to find and recognise the recipient?

2. Can the messenger remember and repeat the message accurately?

3. Will the messenger remember to pass the message if a long interval is involved?

4. What must the messenger do if the recipient is not to be found?

5. How is the originator to know the message has been received?

Which transmission system the Manager uses will depend very much on the circumstances, as not everyone is accessible by phone, and staff rotas often mean messages have to be left, but her communication will be more likely to reach its destination intact if she selects the best system available and anticipates its shortcomings. She should also remember that not all messages are urgent and that it is often wiser to delay sending a non-urgent message until an efficient system is available than employ and inefficient one there and then.

Encoding/decoding signals. Conversations, memos and messages all involve the use of words, either written or spoken, but the choice of vocabulary is vital. In this respect the officer-in-charge must consider her recipient and select her words accordingly. 'Short-term rotating care' is a meaningful phrase to use in conversation with a social worker, but to the non-professional daughter of an elderly person it may conjure up a variety of images. The use of long words or professional jargon, can often be an ego trip at the expense of efficient communications, for few people like admitting they cannot understand. By taking care in encoding her signals a Manager can facilitate decoding by her recipient, a process she can further assist by ensuring she has the recipient's full attention. This she can do by avoiding attempts to communicate the message when her recipient is:

1. Concentrating on other things, such as work or going home.

2. Distracted by events happening around her, such as constant interruptions.

3. Anxious to say something herself.

4. Emotionally unreceptive - being angry or tired, for example.

5. Assimilating another piece of information i.e. being told many things at once.

No one can pay attention to an incoming message when their thoughts are elsewhere. Commanding the attention of the recipient is a vital aspect of communication.

The receiving end of communication

Up to now communications have been considered as they occur in an outward direction from the Manager, but good communications in a Residential Home involve much more than this. If a Home Manager is to manage effectively then she must develop the skill of hearing and absorbing messages coming from others. It is a common fault amongst managers that they spend far too much energy speaking and not enough time listening - listening and internalising what is being said. Within every home there are, for example, residents' opinions to be heeded; inspecting officers' advice to be guided by; instructions from 'superiors' (management committees, owners) to be acted upon; and the views of all staff to be carefully considered. Encouraging people to talk, and listening attentively to their views is an essential facet of the managerial role, and how effectively it is done is a diagnostic feature of the Manager's personal management style. Although a Manager cannot compel the residents or co-workers to approach her and talk freely, she certainly can give them every encouragement and avoid situations that will actually deter them. To these ends the following suggestions to Home Managers are worthy of consideration.

1. Be easily available. If necessary establish a standing period when visits to the office are known to be welcomed. There is nothing more off-putting for residents and staff than constantly finding their Head busy whenever they wish to talk.

2. Ensure conversations can take place in private. Not all topics are personal ones, but many people avoid talking freely if they know they are being overheard.

3. Minimise interruptions. Make it known you are engaged and remember telephones butt into conversations without warning, so have calls transferred to another point or use a room without a phone, when a lengthy conversation is anticipated.

4. Give people a welcome. Making people comfortable and showing concern in them generally is an important prelude to a satisfactory talk.

5. Give obvious attention. Not only is this good manners but an open display of interest is a most potent stimulant to a person's conversation.

6. Ask relevant questions. This is not only an indication of interest but a means of introducing secondary topics.

7. Treat people with respect. Never belittle anyone's ideas or contributions, however unsuitable they may be. The next ones they have could be good, and offended people may be a long time returning.

8. Avoid a superior attitude. The status gap can be a most effective barrier to communications leading to apathy or frustration. 'It's no use talking to her, she knows too much - or thinks she does.'

9. Take action when appropriate. Either act upon suggestions, complaints and requests, or explain convincingly why it is not possible. Conversations that result in no action are not only futile but counter-pro-

ductive. 'She listens all right, but she never does anything' is a common accusation and an indictment of management.

10. Conclude conversations properly. Show appreciation for people's contributions and ask them to return when they wish.

Although these are but common-sense suggestions to promote and sustain incoming communications, it is surprising how easily they can be overlooked by busy managers to everyone's detriment.

4.5 Staff meetings

The next aspect of communications to consider is the role of staff meetings. Too often their occurrence is spasmodic, the staff only being assembled when the manager has specific information to pass on or a grievance demands airing in public. Although these are valid reasons for staff meetings, regular meetings can achieve much more than the mere dissemination of notices and can often prevent grievances growing. Regular staff meetings can:

1. Enable staff of all grades to meet colleagues they rarely encounter in normal working hours, leading to better understanding and closer relations.

2. Foster team spirit and improve morale.

3. Encourage more honest opinion (there is safety in numbers).

4. Lead to a pooling of resources.

5. Raise dormant questions.

6. Increase the accessibility of the officer-in-charge.

7. Develop people's self-confidence.

8. Stimulate wider discussions of residents' needs.

Effective staff meetings are ideal situations for initiating two-way communications, but they are a habit that needs to be developed, and staff unused to regular open meetings will need exposure to several before the benefits are felt. Before adopting the practice of regular meetings, or changing the emphasis of existing meetings away from the mere delivery of notices towards more open discussions, a Manager may find the following advice helpful:

1. Give ample notice of future meetings.

2. Give consideration to all shifts by calling meetings at different times.

3. Keep meetings on a regular basis, even if there appears nothing to discuss. When staff meet they always talk and it is usually about work.

4. Meetings need not be formal with a written agenda or accurate minutes. Informal meetings are usually more conducive to spontaneous discussion.

5. Staff meetings are to discuss matters pertaining directly to the home. They are not union branch meetings and this distinction should be clear.

6. Even in informal meetings, a chairman or group leader is essential to maintain friendly order by preventing the more vocal members dominating discussions, by restricting topics to the relevant, and by drawing meetings to a close, but the person-in-charge need not always be the Chairman. Staff meetings are not the Manager's meetings and more productive discussions may come from meetings where the Manager is present but not in the chair. By the same token, meetings should not be cancelled simply because the Manager is not available. Furthermore, learning to chair meetings is part of staff development.

7. The Home's Manager should be prepared for opinions that conflict with her own and be willing to act upon staff suggestions wherever possible. No manager has all the right answers and one purpose of staff meetings is to pool resources.

8. The Manager should not be deterred from continuing with regular meetings by initial poor attendance. Some staff may have a low opinion of meetings from past experience and be awaiting the views of their colleagues before attending themselves.

9. Meetings arranged to precede a social evening can increase attend-ance without detracting from the value of the meeting itself.

10. Some staff meetings can be used to introduce departmental personnel the staff rarely meet, such as social workers, training officers or homes advisers; this can be valuable and stimulating to all parties.

11. Meetings should not be allowed to continue beyond a predeter-mined hour. Staff have a right to know when meetings will end and their continuing attendance may depend on this.

Although staff meetings are an ideal medium for group discussions, they are not suitable for more direct and personal discussions between the Home Manager and staff. Individuals who are attending training courses, new recruits to the team, people with personal difficulties and staff who never approach the Head of their own volition are amongst those with special needs which require the Manager to initiate individual interviews. These people should be seen frequently as long as their special condition persists. Suggestions given herein apply to the conduct of these interviews, the only difference being that the staff have been requested to attend. (This type of interview should not be confused with disciplinary interviews which are a special consideration for which specific procedures are laid down by employing authorities).

In considering communications in residential homes for the elderly there is the great danger of concentrating on the staff to the exclusion of the residents, the very people for whose benefit the Home is established. Seldom is a structure organised to receive their contributions, let alone stimulate their thoughts, on the management of the Home. Admittedly an increasing incidence of mental infirmity and physical frailty makes their participation seem impossible to achieve, but their group potential is too often underestimated, and in consequence little is attempted.

Although many residents may be severely restricted in their capacity to grasp what is expected, most Homes have a nucleus of residents who are both alert and articulate. Such residents can, indeed should, form the basis of a resident's council, and the fact that not all residents have the capacity to take part should not preclude those who have from enjoying this function.

The actual terms of reference for a resident's council will depend very much on their interests, ability and experience, but it must be reasonable to argue that whatever affects their life in the home is their legitimate concern. To this end they should be encouraged to discuss any matter of interest to them and make their views known to the Home Manager or official visitors of the managing authority.

Of course the residents do not own the Home. They just live there, and representatives of the managing authority are governed by policy decisions and constrained by limited resources. But, this should not prevent residents voicing their opinions simply because difficulties might follow. If the residents feel strongly about something they have a right to be properly heard and they are just as capable of being reasonable in the face of sound argument as anyone else. A Residents Council should be free to discuss any topic it chooses, but its function should not be restricted to discussion alone. There are several aspects of the Home's management it could actually control, for example:

a. The spending of money in the comforts fund.

b. The frequency and destination of resident's outings.

c. The timing of meals.

d. The selection of room decorations, from choices presented.

Full meetings with all residents present need not be frequent affairs. As with many societies, much work could be delegated to an elected committee which can meet as often as it feels necessary. A Manager who wishes to develop a residents council in her Home must be prepared initially to invest effort in establishing a committee, possibly in the face of much apathy. Residents accustomed to being totally organised will display considerable inertia at first. But once they realise that they can effectively influence life in the Home and their confidence grows, their meetings will become lively and productive. Problems will undoubtedly arise with residents arguing amongst themselves, complaints abounding and impossible requests put forward, but these are signs of life to be welcomed, and many positive suggestions can also arise.

CHAPTER 5
Managing the Home II

STAFF RECRUITMENT AND SELECTION

'The shortage of suitable men and women to staff the residential homes is one of the serious factors in the present situation, for so many other problems - overwork, lack of regular free time, cancelled holidays, etc - are directly connected with it.'

Most managers of residential homes for the elderly have suffered the effects of staff shortages and will closely identify with these sentiments, even though they were expressed a long time ago in the William's Report (National Council for Social Services 'Caring for People). But the operative phrase is SUITABLE MEN AND WOMEN.

In considering the recruitment and selection of staff, a fundamental managerial function, two closely related factors must be borne in mind: the importance of appointing only suitable people, and the extreme difficulty in doing so.

The difficulty in appointing suitable staff stems from two basic sources - the lack of sufficient people with the right attributes applying for vacancies, and the problem of choosing the right person from those who do apply. But these difficulties must be overcome since the appointment of unsuitable staff can be disastrous from several points of view:

Caring standards. Residents are entitled to be cared for by those who have their welfare at heart and the ability to acquire quickly all the necessary skills. Nothing is more certain to militate against the provision of quality care than the engagement of unsuitable staff, to any position in the home. Such is the intimacy of contact between the cared for and the caring that even a single poor appointment becomes a constant source of frustration.

Existing staff. No one likes working alongside people who are incompetent, lazy, unco-operative, quarrelsome, domineering or simply unhappy at work. Not only do colleagues like this fail to pull their own weight, the friction they cause prevents others from functioning properly.

Public relations. Homes for the elderly have a public image which is assessed more by their fabric and the staff they employ than their residents who are scarcely on view. Just one poorly regarded employee can damage the standing of a Home in the eyes of local inhabitants: 'If that is the type of person who works there, I hope I never have to go in.'

The Home's Manager. Managers everywhere have to live with the mistakes they make. This is singularly true in the case of all staff appointments, but doubly so when staff must work closely with colleagues in the care of vulnerable people. An officer-in-charge has limited time at her disposal and can ill-afford to spend a disproportionate amount of it correcting the mistakes and repairing the damage created by a troublesome colleague. One weak member of staff can consume more of her managerial effort than all her better staff put together.

Employment Legislation. Unsatisfactory staff can be dismissed, but they must be dismissed in a way that accords with the law. European legislation is increasingly widening its arms to embrace categories of employees who were formerly outside of employment protection. Media coverage disseminates the new rules and employees are more aware of their rights.

This must not deter a Home Manager from divesting herself of the services of an unsatisfactory employee, but in doing this she must follow the correct procedures. Failure to do so may result in her having to plead her case at an Industrial Tribunal where she will need evidence to support her actions. All this is time consuming, when time is at a premium. Far better not to have appointed the person in the first place.

The case for making satisfactory appointments is self-evident, but the means of doing so another matter. The selection of good staff in any situation is fraught with difficulties and no one can guarantee to be right every time. This is particularly true in the case of residential homes for the elderly where most positions, especially at care staff level, do not demand formal qualifications and appointments have to be made on the basis of an estimation of the candidate's worth.

The absence of formal qualifications for care staff not only fails to provide guide lines for appointments, but also encourages many potentially unsuitable people to apply for advertised vacancies.

There are those who feel that working in a residential home is nothing more than housework, with an elderly parent living in, but on a larger scale. Most applicants realise they should express a desire to work with people but a percentage of these, in the words of the William's Report '. . . do not possess the insight and humility and the respect for the individuality of those in their care which would make them refrain from a too authoritarian attitude toward them.'

Whilst it might be unrealistic, as the same report suggests, to expect part-time workers, whose principal concern is to care for their own households and families, to have the range of qualities of the more senior staff, it should be expected of them that they have the capacity to give genuine respect for the independence and individuality of those for whom they are caring, and to be aware of their social and personal problems.

Given these presenting factors only a carefully considered and systematic approach to the appointment of staff can reduce errors in staff selection to a minimum.

A Manager who has the delegated authority to make her own appointments needs to be aware of the various stages of recruitment and selection. These stages should be followed for whatever level of vacancy is to be filled. Part time staff, working but a few hours a week, can have an equally detrimental effect on the Home, if the wrong people are selected, as those working longer hours.

1. Review of staffing.

2. Job description.

3. Job specification.

4. Advertising.

5. Shortlisting.

6. Obtaining references.

7. Interviewing.

8. Probationary period.

These stages which are explored in greater detail below, may seem to involve considerable time for a hard pressed manager, particularly if she is responsible for a smaller home and has many other tasks to perform. In such circumstances, and when a vacancy arises with little warning, there may be a strong temptation to abbreviate or by-pass procedures. Despite the immanence of short term inconvenience this temptation should be resisted. Even when a Manager is aware of an interested and seemingly suitable replacement she should advertise the vacancy properly; her responsibility to her residents demands that she engages not a reasonably able person quickly, but the most competent person possible. It is far better for existing staff to be asked to undertake overtime work, or for some non-essential tasks to be delayed, than it is for an unsuitable person to be introduced to the home.

The Home Manager who plans ahead can reduce the time involved in going through the correct procedures by producing proformas, which can then be filled in for vacancies as they arise. Simple but useful proformas can be designed to cover job descriptions, job specifications, obtaining references by direct questions, shortlisting and interviewing. There is an additional advantage in having such forms, particularly for the short listing and interview stages, in that they produce fileable records of the reasons why certain individuals were interviewed and appointed, and others not. This information will prove valuable should an unsuccessful applicant claim to have been unlawfully discriminated against, as is increasingly happening.

5.1 Review of staffing.

When an employee resigns it is an opportunity to review staffing in the Home. The Home Manager should ask herself if she needs to replace the person leaving with some one to do exactly the same type of work for the same number of hours; or is this the chance to split a full time post into two new part time appointments. She may even consider deploying the hours to existing part time staff who she has identified as giving good service. Another possibility is to change the nature or emphasis of the job if, say she wants to introduce some social activities to her home to help meet one of her objectives. In many instances circumstances may dictate that she brings in an identical replacement, and quickly, but the wise managers does not let this opportunity to review her staffing slip by.

5.2 Job Description.

Although formats vary in style, these usually contain the following information:

Job title

Job location

Job summary

Main duties

People responsible to and responsible for In-service training

Terms and conditions of employment

5.3 Job Specification.

From the job description a job specification (sometimes called a personnel specification) is compiled to indicate those personal qualities and skills required in a person for the efficient performance of the work described. As with the job description this is usually structured under specific headings such as:

Age range

Qualifications

Relevant experience

Health/physique

Personality

Availability for in-service training

The list of specifications may be longer or shorter, according to the nature of the post, and an embellishment is to express them in two categories:

(a) essential, if they are really required.

(b) desirable, if not essential but the Manager would prefer someone with them.

When a job specification is being compiled, the specifications should be restricted to relevant qualities and skills. There is no advantage in stipulating qualifications in excess of those required (bearing in mind future prospects of promotion), since people who are more highly qualified than their position requires seldom stay long in the job. Furthermore it limits the number of suitable applicants. The profile created in the job specification should bear a sensible relationship.

Once the job description and the job specification have been compiled, a major contribution has been made to the selection process. The information contained in them can then be condensed to form an advertisement and the job specification used as a basis for selecting the most appropriate candidate at the interview stage.

5.4 Advertising.

The purpose of making known a job vacancy is to attract the maximum number of suitable applicants (since not to do so is just as big a failing of the selection procedure as the appointment of the wrong person at the interview stage) but not to receive a large number of applications irrespective of their suitability for the position. Initially an advertisement need only stimulate potentially interested people to request additional information, for they can then be supplied with copies of the job description and job specification to help them decide whether the vacancy appeals to them and whether their existing qualifications justify them making an application. To this end a simple, attractive and unambiguous advertisement is required stating - name of organisation, job title, job location, essential qualifications, renumeration, and how to obtain further information. Lengthy advertisements are costly and often too closely worded to be eye-catching.

Generally speaking the greater the publicity the greater the response and a variety of media can be employed, depending upon the nature of the vacancy. In addition to newspapers, professional journals, job centres and local radio stations all have valuable roles to play. Neither should the value of word of mouth advertising be underestimated but only as a supplement to other forms of advertising.

Although the cost of advertising must be carefully considered, a little extra expense in advertising is abundantly repaid if it results in the appointment of a better person who would otherwise have been missed. Good residential staff are a scarce commodity and well worth searching for.

Many managers in large organisations may have little direct influence over the placing of advertisements, when advertising is the function of their department's personnel section, but this does not mean it is not their concern, and they should make known to their superiors during management meetings any reservations and constructive criticisms they may have.

5.5 Short-listing Candidates.

Only a limited number of candidates can be efficiently and effectively interviewed for a single appointment because of the time and expense involved and the difficulties inherent in trying to compare too many people when decision time comes.

From the applications received it will therefore be necessary to compile a short list of applicants to be interviewed. The time taken to prepare a short list will depend both upon the size of the response and the variety of applicants, but in all cases the following guidance applies:

Application forms should not be considered until after the closure date to avoid prejudging early applicants.

Each application should be carefully compared with the job specification and those which do not meet the minimum standards required eliminated.

The remaining applications should then be reconsidered to isolate the interview candidates. These candidates should not be ranked in order of preference for there can be no favourites at this preliminary stage of selection.

Only those applicants who appear by their applications to be properly qualified for the job should be invited for interview. Requesting unsuitable applicants to attend to make up a 'respectable' number of interviewees wastes everyone's time.

All applicants rejected for the interview should be re-scrutinised to ensure no likely applicant has been overlooked.

It is not an easy task to discriminate between applications, whether the vacancy is for a deputy, domestic, cook or care assistant, as many of the qualities looked for in staff of an elderly persons' home are not readily discernible from a letter or application form. This is likely to be the case if the form is a standard one, not used by the home exclusively, but by the employer for all manner of appointments and which requests irrelevant details, as far as the home's manager is concerned, at the expense of more useful information.

Details of age, sex, marital status, qualifications and relevant experience can be read directly from the application, but other equally vital features have to be gleaned by closer examination and a home's manager may like to make out a check list to assist with her scrutiny of application forms. The examples can be added to from personal experience.

Check list for scrutinising application forms

1. Communication

Is the application written clearly using sound expressions and adequate vocabulary?

2. Motivation

Has the applicant taken care to write her application neatly, accurately and with a desire to impress?

3. Sincerity

Has the applicant given reasons for applying and if so are they appropriate? If she has had no previous experience in residential work, has she taken steps to acquaint herself in any way with the nature of the work?

4. Stability

How many previous jobs has the applicant had recently?

5. Training

Is there any indication the applicant has willingly undertaken training whilst at work, even if previous jobs are not relevant to residential care?

6. People

Has the applicant's previous jobs involved her in giving service to others?

7. Transport

Is her address conveniently situated for travelling to work?

8. Social

Does the applicant's social activities suggest inclinations or attributes that indicate she would make an agreeable colleague?

Check list questions like these help the Manager to scrutinise application forms by focusing her mind on those qualities, aptitudes and personal circumstances she has previously identified as being desirable in candidates to be shortlisted. However because of their subjective nature, care must be taken in deducing information from them; for instance frequent changes in jobs may have been occasioned by a husband moving areas in his work and the possession of personal transport can easily overcome the problems of a more distant address. Nevertheless such exploration of an application is useful in screening applicants and in indicating areas to be probed in greater depth should an applicant subsequently be called for an interview.

5.6 References.

The practice of approaching named referees varies in different organisations. Some employers prefer to contact referees during the short-listing process, whilst others like to wait until candidates have been interviewed, when the references can be used to confirm a selection. The latter course avoids interviewers prejudicing candidates before they are interviewed, but as referees have much to offer, when used properly, it is probably wiser to contact them at the pre-interview stage.

References may be obtained in a variety of ways.

(a) Non-specific references. These are obtained by writing to one or more of the referees, named by the applicant in her application, requesting the referee to comment on the suitability of the applicant for the post.

It is usual to enclose with the request a copy of the job description and the job specification to guide the referee. Whilst this approach is quick and simple it does have several disadvantages which the manager should be aware of.

No applicant will knowingly have named a hostile referee and no referee is likely to openly obstruct a person he has agreed with to support. Non-specific references are therefore likely to dwell on, even exaggerate, the good qualities of an applicant whilst and studiously ignoring their weaker ones. It is for this reason that what is not put in a reference of this type is often more informative than what is included.

The status of the person providing the reference can increase or diminish the value of a reference. Those provided by an employer, or previous employer, are more likely to be useful indicators of the applicant's potential worth than those written by friends, associates or the local religious leader (unless, in the last instance, purely a character reference is being sought). This is why it is usual to stipulate on an application form that one of the referees must be a previous employer of the applicant.

If a manager is using this method then having received a reference she should not overlook the merits of contacting by telephone the referee to ask for more details or to clarify any ambiguities there may be, should she think this necessary.

(b) Specific references. Unlike non-specific references, that have left it to the discretion of referees what points to cover and what to ignore, specific references contain responses to direct questions. To obtain such a reference the home's manager needs to have prepared a form on which are written the questions she would like answers to. Examples of possible areas to seek information on are given below:

Name and address of employer

Position held by applicant as (when) an employee

Length of service

Health record

Punctuality

Reliability

Honesty

Attitude towards management

Working relationships with co-workers

Quality of work

Reason for leaving employer

Opinion on suitability for job applied for

Would employer employ the employee again

If the Manager is taking up a reference from a referee who has not employed the applicant then she will have to use a separate set of questions. She will wish to know the status of the referee, whether he is related to the applicant, and the nature and length of their acquaintance. These are elementary questions to ask, but the answers are important to establish the credibility of the reference, and it is surprising how often they are overlooked. Other questions should seek comments, for example, on the applicant's personality, reliability, honesty, social activities and there should be a space on the form for the referee to give his reasons why the applicant is suited to the job.

(c) Verbal references. This method, usually done over the telephone, has only one advantage - its speed. When a true emergency situation demands that someone is engaged quickly it enables a home's manager to obtain a reference and thus not commit the cardinal sin of taking an employee on without the precaution of consulting a referee to safeguard herself, staff and residents. Verbal references on their own have serious drawbacks. They do not give the referee, taken by surprise with a telephone call, time to make a considered response and there is no documentary evidence should this be needed in the future. Verbal references are best avoided, but if used the referee should be asked to confirm his opinion in writing, using either of the two methods described above.

5.7 Interviews.

Selection by interview is a most subjective process and there is no formula that will guarantee success. However fallibilities inherent in the process can be reduced by careful planning and by the interviewers being aware both of their own prejudices and of common failings in interviews.

A Home Manager would be advised to reflect upon the following criticisms frequently levelled at interviewers.

a. Interviewers are generally unprepared for the interview and have not thought out appropriate questions to ask. With panel interviews the members have not rehearsed amongst themselves who is to ask what and for what purpose.

b. They are uncertain of the qualities they are looking for.

c. They make up their minds about candidates in the first few minutes and then spend the rest of the interview searching for evidence to justify their premature decision.

d. They judge others by their own subjective feelings. 'I'm good, she's like me, therefore she must be good.'

e. They fail to extract from the candidates (particularly the nervous ones) all the information they need to make a sound decision.

Whether a Manager is conducting an interview herself, or is a member of a panel of selectors, she is the one who has to live with any errors made, and it is her Residential Home that will suffer, so she must be properly prepared for an interview, either to conduct it herself or help mitigate the mistakes of others. The following points may assist:

a. From the job specification prepare a clear list of the qualities required in the successful candidates.

b. Prepare a wide list of questions to elicit the general information required.

c. Re-examine each application form and note additional areas that need probing with each individual candidate.

d. If a panel of interviewers is involved, discuss the conduct of the interview and the sequence of questioning.

e. Arrange for a suitable interview room that will be free from interruptions and which looks business-like without being too formal.

f. Make arrangements for candidates to be received and have a room available for them to wait. Candidates should be welcomed properly, shown where the cloakroom is, and given a drink.

After these careful preparations, the conduct of the actual interview must be considered. The interviewees are invariably nervous and need setting at ease, so it must be remembered that the function of an interview is to encourage them to talk purposefully about themselves. The art of conducting interviews can only be developed with practice, but a Home Manager can improve her technique by considering the following suggestions:

* All relevant papers, job specification, application forms, prepared questions etc - should be to hand.

* Initial questions should be easy to answer and show the interviewer's interest in the candidate.

* Subsequent questions should demand a structural reply. 'Yes' or 'No' answers are most unproductive.

* Replies must be carefully listened to, they may not be the ones anticipated, and a supplementary question may quickly be required.

* Interest should be shown all the time a candidate is talking to encourage her to develop her points. A smile, a nod or even a grunt can accomplish this without recourse to continual questions.

* Silent periods should not be interrupted too quickly, the candidate may be thinking of her reply, and it is a useful time to gauge her reactions. (On the other hand the candidate must not be allowed to become distressed by a question she cannot answer.)

* Much can be gained in panel interviews by watching the candidate's reaction to a colleague's question.

* Rapport, so essential in interviews, should not be destroyed by note taking. Observations can be recorded at the end of each interview.

* All relevant areas should be thoroughly probed, even if this involves taking longer than the scheduled time.

* A candidate should be asked if she has any questions to raise, in a positive, inviting manner not as an after thought. Candidate's questions can be very revealing.

* The interview should be conducted in such a way that the candidate leaves feeling she has enjoyed a fair hearing and with polite thanks for her trouble.

When each candidate has been interviewed notes should be made for reference for it is easy to confuse candidates at the end of a series of interviews. Research would indicate that first and last candidates are remembered best. At the conclusion of the interviews a decision should be made on the basis of all relevant information, with prejudices controlled, and the best candidate offered the position. It is however better not to appoint at all than to select even the best person if there are doubts over her suitability.

If the decision is made whilst the candidates are still present, once the successful person has accepted the position, the remainder should be informed tactfully and thanked properly in a way that does credit to the home or department. If the decision is reached after the candidates have departed the unsuccessful candidates and all other applicants should be promptly and politely informed. Too often the reputation of an organisation suffers because unsuccessful applicants are not informed of the results of their applications.

Staff selection is of vital importance in management. No home's manager, however capable or hardworking she may be, can run a home properly without the assistance of good staff, and no amount of subsequent activity can ever compensate for a poor appointment.

5.7 Probationary Period

As previously pointed out the interview system is far from perfect and even the most experienced of managers make mistakes from time to time. This eventuality can be insured against, to a large degree, by pointing out to all applicants that there will be a probationary period for the person appointed during which her employment may be terminated, if she is not deemed to be satisfactory, without the need for the employer to give detailed reasons. If a clause to this effect, stipulating a period of, say, six months, is put in the employee's contract of employment then the Manager may more comfortably dismiss the person who does not measure up. An individual may be considered unsuitable for any of several reasons that are very difficult to substantiate with objective evidence, but the Manager is nonetheless aware that the employee is not right for the Home. It would, however, be bad practice for a Manager to terminate a probationer's employment, when due to shortcomings, without first letting the probationer know what these are, and giving opportrnities for improvement. Unless, of course, the failures are such that a quick dismissal is the only proper option available.

CHAPTER 6
Staff In-service Training

6.1 Introduction

Without the aid of a properly structured training programme the time and effort a Home Manager invests in the recruitment and selection of staff will be largely wasted. Training is required to convert potentially able, but inexperienced recruits, into useful members of staff and to increase the effectiveness of the more established workers - since none can rightly claim to have mastered all the knowledge and skills needed to care for the frail elderly.

How quickly a new member of staff can become effective, making a significant contribution to life within the Home, depends entirely upon how well that person is trained while at work. Few, if any, people entering residential services for the first time have the range of skills or depth of understanding necessary to care adequately for the frail elderly. Maybe their previous experience has been limited to the care of their own families or if they have worked in the hospital services been restricted to a discipline much narrower than residential care. Even those desirable recruits coming from pre-service training courses at colleges, such as General National Vocational Qualifications (GNVQs), will lack many specific skills or sufficient practice in them to make them immediately competent at work.

Unfortunately a systematic approach to skills training for new recruits is sadly absent in many residential homes, with unjustifiable confidence being placed either in the process of learning gradually by experience, or in a brief period of 'sitting next to Nellie'. Learning by experience involves making mistakes, which cannot by tolerated when the welfare of others is at stake and the effectiveness of 'sitting next to Nellie' is entirely dependent upon the time, interest and skills Nellie has to bring to her task. Undoubtedly there is much a capable, experienced member of staff can teach a new colleague, but unless the teacher has undergone formal training and the teaching is properly structured and monitored it will be of indeterminate value.

It is not only new recruits who are disadvantaged by the lack of in-service training. Established staff are assumed to be competent by virtue of their years of experience, when in fact they may be far from being so, thus putting themselves and the residents at risk. Equally disadvantaged is the Home's Manager, for without trained staff to train new recruits she finds that they quickly absorb the levels of the existing untrained workers and the same low quality of care is perpetuated, whatever the staff changeover rate is. It is only through structured training that the Manager can reach the high standards aspired to.

In the growing competitive world of residential care provision, where Homes are regularly inspected - with the reports made public and establishments vie for the attention of purchasers of care, those Homes that employ competent staff and through them offer quality care are far more likely to succeed.

This commercial reason alone should itself dictate the adoption of a systematic training policy, but it is not the only reason. By offering formal training opportunities to the staff a Manager will achieve many benefits:

Trained staff work more effectively.

Trained staff feel valued by management, morale is higher.

Trained staff feel greater commitment, turnover rates are reduced.

Diagnosing in-service training needs and then arranging for these needs to be met, are essential management functions. A Manager may wish to consider three stages for a structured in-service training programme - induction, basic training and NVQ awards.

6.2 Induction Training

Induction is the process of integrating new recruits into an organisation. Its purpose is to assist new employees in finding their bearings, establishing working/social relations with colleagues, understanding the nature of their duties and what is expected of them, and generally passing smoothly into the established routine. Without adequate induction new employees, all of whom arrive with a measure of apprehension, experience trauma in their initial days, however pleasant the existing staff may appear to be. When, as is frequently the case in residential work, new employees are entering a strange world of which they have had no relevant experience, this period can be particularly unnerving. If they are to be encouraged to feel confident in their new environment by making early a significant contribution to work, then they require proper induction.

Various organisations differ in their approach to induction, some managers arrange elaborate courses extending over days for their new employees, whereas others are content to leave individuals to cope as best they can, after giving them a perfunctory welcome, and trust blindly in the good nature of their subordinates to initiate newcomers.

New recruits to a Residential Home are seldom treated to a structured induction period, more often, like the last example, they are expected to 'pick up the ropes' by watching their colleagues and asking advice. Not only is this a discourteous way of treating new members of the team, it is wasteful of time and potentially damaging to the staff and residents alike. Although there are natural limits to how much new people can absorb in their first days at work there is a minimum of information and support they all require if they are to feel welcomed, wanted and useful. The following points can assist a Home's Manager in planning an induction programme for a new employee.

a. Note the name of the new employee and the time she is expected to report. It is most disconcerting for a new person to be met with a look of surprise or a hesitantly remembered name, and worse still not to be met at all.

b. Be free of all other commitments to devote time to her induction.

c. Have a list of points ready to discuss with her, for apart from the mechanics of ensuring she is properly on the payroll she will, for her own reassurance, need to understand:

* The broad aims of the Home

* The accepted routine

*The nature of the work and what is expected of her

* The areas in which she might experience difficulty and what to do if she does

* The importance of safety regulations affecting herself, the residents and colleagues

* Who her immediate superiors are

d. Walk around the Home with her so that she can find her bearings and meet the residents. Be prepared to discuss with her points that arise from her observations.

e. Introduce her informally to the staff. Because she will find it difficult at first to remember many new names or relate to a lot of strange faces, have one member of staff prepared to befriend her and to whom she can turn easily for sound advice in her early days at work.

f. Explain what she is to do for the rest of the day.

g. Arrange to see her again, before she leaves the home, to discuss any uncertainties that have arisen during the day and to give her her duties for the following shift.

h. Make arrangements to meet her at agreed times during her first month to discuss her reactions, but advise her that she may approach you whenever she wishes.

For a Manager to make arrangements for a structured induction, even along the simple lines suggested above, requires the expenditure of considerable time; but it is time well spent. If a busy manager overlooks the apprehensions of a new employee and fails to give her the support she needs, then she runs the risk of clouding the recruit's whole attitude to work, her approach to residents and her opinion of the manager by giving her a poor first impression of the Home.

6.3 Basic Training

Induction is, of necessity, a brief affair, its purpose is to help integrate a new employee quickly and pleasantly into the routine of the Home. What it achieves is important and valuable, but it is a preliminary to, not a substitute for, further in-service training.

All new employees need to be taught early in their employment the essential procedures of residential care both in a manner in which they can absorb the instruction and at a level governed by their previous experience. To plan a basic training programme for her staff a Manager should first identify the separate elements of their work and then list the specific skills and knowledge needed for the satisfactory performance of each task. From this exercise a short training programme can then be devised to meet the particular needs of individuals by covering those areas in which their skills or knowledge are deficient. Some relevant knowledge and skill areas are:

1. Basic human needs and their simple application to caring situations eg. privacy and knocking on doors; independence and encouraging residents to achieve within their limits; self-respect and the need to address residents courteously.

2. The concept of confidentiality.

3. Lifting procedures and the correct use of aids.

4. Precautions with medicines.

5. Essential first aid.

6. Simple techniques in observing residents.

7. Personal hygiene.

8. Nature of confusion and how to react to the confused.

9. Attitudes to dying and death.

10. Receiving visitors.

Since the areas selected for basic training are most likely to be covered in depth later during National Vocational Qualification (NVQ) training there is no need for basic training in the Home to be an external affair; it is sufficient for the selected topics to be broached simply and informally. But it is vital for the confidence of the staff and the safety of the residents that they are covered. How the Home's Manager approaches each topic will depend upon the topic itself, her own interests and skills and the presence of experienced staff willing to help with basic training of new staff. Topics like confidentiality could be discussed with the Manager over coffee and practical skills such as the correct use of aids could be delegated to a competent, experienced employee. The training methods adopted by the Manager do not matter provided they are effective in giving adequate basic training.

6.4 National Vocational Qualifications (NVQs)

A gentle warning to all readers from this point forward: do not be afraid of the initials employed (and over-employed!) in the following descriptions. These are used, of course, as abbreviations of cumbersome titles given to qualifications and qualifying institutions. In time, you will learn those most relevant to you, and become familiar with their usage in an easy-going way.

Since Managing To Care was first written there has been a fundamental change in in-service training opportunities for residential care staff, at all levels of operation. For senior staff, seeking a recognised professional qualification, the former Certificate in Social Service has been replaced by the Diploma in Social Work. But of even greater significance is the recent development of National Vocational Qualifications (NVQs). These new qualifications are now the only in-service qualifications available to care staff.

The introduction of NVQs is already having considerable impact upon residential care and their effect will be increasingly felt as the NVQ initiative gathers momentum. The only true decision facing a Home's management is not whether to become involved with NVQs, but when to become involved. And this is a decision that cannot long be delayed for NVQs will, undoubtedly, increase the effectiveness of care staff and by this raise the standards of care practise. Apart from improving the quality of life of the residents, in itself sufficient reason for embracing training through NVQs, all managers of private/voluntary homes and increasingly those in the public sector, are daily conscious of the commercial forces at play that insist they match their Homes' standards to those of best. Quality assurance has penetrated at last into residential care and will become the key to survival.

As new NVQs are being developed all the time, and existing ones modified, it follows that anything written on them may quickly become dated in detail. However both the principles on which they are formulated and their structures are likely to remain constant.

Some Homes' managers, particularly those working in larger organisations, are already familiar with NVQs and have staff pursuing the awards - for these managers what follows may be of little interest. The next few pages are written for those who have but a passing awareness of the development and structure of NVQs and who need to be in a position to discuss them more knowledgeably. Decisions, particularly vital decisions, as in any competent manager knows, cannot be made well if made without essential information.

Development of National Vocational Qualifications

NVQs had their conception in a 1981 publication, issued by the former Manpower Services Commission (MSC), and entitled *New Training Initiative: Agenda for Action*. This publication recognised that Britain had serious problems with vocational training and needed a strategy to develop a 'flexible, adaptable workforce to cope with the uncertainties that cloud the future'. This strategy was to involve three principle objectives:

Develop skills training

Equip all young people for work

Widen opportunities for adults

But more significantly the publication stated the urgent need to develop standards of a new kind.

These new type of standards were later to emerge as work based competencies and the flexible, adaptable workforce became defined as a competent workforce.

The need to overhaul vocational qualifications was recognised in the publication *Review Of Vocational Qualifications In England And Wales (MSC/NEDC 1986)*. This review made serious criticisms of the current system of vocational qualifications. It complained that there was a plethora of vocational awards issued by a variety of bodies that created confusion in the minds of employers and those seeking training. It identified lack of training provision in some areas and considerable overlaps in others. The Review pointed out that existing awards concentrated too much on knowledge and too little on those work based skills regarded as important by employers. It also acknowledged that these existing, knowledge based qualifications placed too many barriers in the way of those seeking training - barriers such as age, entry qualifications and time taken to attend courses - and that they failed to allow trainees to undertake their training in stages by awarding credits for parts successfully completed.

The Review recommended that in future vocational qualifications should be characterised by statements of competence that were seen to be relevant to work and which would facilitate entry into, or progression in employment, further education and training, and be issued by a recognised body.

A government White Paper entitled *Working Together, Education and Training (HMSO 1986)* accepted the recommendations of the Review and later created the NATIONAL COUNCIL FOR VOCATIONAL QUALIFICATIONS (NCVQ) to usher in a radical reform of vocational training in England and Wales.

The NCVQ was set some very specific tasks:

Establish standards of occupational competence to meet

the full range of employment, including self-employment,

and to ensure that vocational qualifications are based

on them.

Design and implement a new national framework for

vocational qualifications.

Accredit bodies to make awards.

Ensure the awarding bodies cover all occupational areas.

Secure arrangements for quality assurance.

Set up effective liaison with bodies awarding vocational

qualifications.

Undertake, or arrange to be undertaken, research and

development to discharge these functions.

Promote vocational education, training and qualifications

and spread good practice.

In Northern Ireland and Scotland the EDUCATION AND TRAINING UNIT, and the SCOTTISH VOCATIONAL EDUCATION COUNCIL (SCOTVEC) respectively have similar responsibilities. NVQs and their Scottish equivalent SVQs employ the same national standards and are designed to be mutually recognised throughout the UK. Any reference to NVQs in this chapter therefore applies equally to SVQs. To help it discharge its responsibilities the NCVQ began to approve a Lead Body (LB) for each recognised occupational area. New LBs are being formed all the time.

Lead Bodies

A LB is an employer-led organisation representing the views of employers, trades unions and other interested parties within a given occupational area. Its purpose is to bring about the development of industry-defined standards of occupational competence.

The LB for public and private sectors of health and social services and the voluntary sector is the Care Sector Consortium.

Although a LB is responsible for the development of standards for occupational competencies and NVQs within its occupational area, the development of these standards has to be through a project undertaken by practitioners/managers with the assistance of someone with expertise in writing competence-based standards. The Residential, Domiciliary and Day Care Project (RDDC) and the Health Care Support Workers Project (HCSW) separately produced standards for their respective fields. The Integration Project, later established by the Care Sector Consortium, integrated the awards.

All NVQs developed by an LB have to be approved by the NCVQ before they can be released.

Awarding Bodies

The NCVQ does not award NVQs: it accredits other bodies to make the awards on its behalf. The awarding body for NVQs in Care are BTEC and the Joint Awarding Body (JAB), comprising CCETSW and C&G. Although the members of the JAB issue NVQ certificates under their own individual examining body name the awards all have equal standing.

All awarding bodies have to comply with stringent conditions laid down by the NCVQ. One of these is that they must participate in the NCVQs Credit Accumulation and Transfer Scheme (CATS). The CATs scheme ensures that not only must awarding bodies certificate the unit parts of NVQs as credits towards the whole NVQ - so that individuals can gain their award over different lengths of time, but that they must also agree to recognise credits issued by other awarding bodies - to facilitate transfer between NVQ training in different occupational areas.

Awarding bodies approve organisations, that meet their own exacting conditions, as approved assessment centres for one or more of the NVQ awards they make.

Assessment Centres

BTEC and the two members of the JAB, responsible to the Care Sector Consortium for validating care awards, approve various organisations as assessment centres. The size of the organisation does not matter, what is important is that it can satisfy the required conditions.

Examples of such organisations are:

A college of further (or higher) education.

A social services department.

A hospital - statutory or private.

A charitable organisation.

A residential home, or group of homes, run by a private owner or a voluntary society

Any of the above organisations may function as an assessment centre in its own right or be part of a consortium with one or more of the others.

Who is eligible for NVQ Integrated Care Awards?

All people working (paid or voluntarily) in recognised situations - providing direct care to people in residential, day, domiciliary and nursing settings - are eligible to register for NVQs in care. This includes part time, temporary and evening shift workers. (Employees working in other occupational areas within a residential home, such as cooks and domestic staff should be encouraged to obtain NVQs in their own occupational areas.)

An important concept to be grasped here is that NVQs are quite unlike traditional courses which specify entry qualifications, require students to follow a particular course of study for a set length of time, often at college or other training centre and then examine the students at the end of the course. NVQ units, and full certificates, are awarded on the sole basis of the demonstration of competent performance in the work place. How an individual reaches that level of competence is not necessarily dependent upon them undergoing a training course; though, of course, varying degrees of assistance will be required at work to enable individuals to develop the necessary competencies. NVQs are about raising the standards of people's competence at work.

What Is Competence and How Does It Have To Be Demonstrated?

Competence is defined as the ability to perform work activities to specified standards.

Within NVQs competence is sub-divided into units of competence, which in turn are composed of elements of competence and it is defined precisely to indicate the standard to which it must be performed.

To be deemed competent for a given element a candidate must demonstrate to a qualified assessor that she can perform a particular work activity to the prescribed standard. In demonstrating this the candidate must also show that she has:

KNOWLEDGE - the theory, principles or information relevant to the activity.

SKILL - the ability to perform the component tasks in their correct sequence, efficiently and effectively by recognising and concentrating on the important issues that lead to achievement.

TRANSFERENCE - the capacity to transfer the above knowledge and skills to new and different situations within the occupational area.

PERSONAL EFFECTIVENESS - the personal qualities to work easily and well with others; managers, co-workers and customers (residents).

What Is Accreditation Of Prior Learning (APL)?

As stated previously NVQs are not training courses in the traditional sense, they are the results of assessments of personal competencies at work. A candidate for a NVQ award can demonstrate the possession of personal competence, other than being directly observed by an assessor, by presenting evidence of competencies previously acquired.

To do this a candidate must:

86

*Request APL from an assessor trained and registered to assess prior learning and establish what type of evidence will satisfy the assessor that the candidate has the relevant competencies. Whole NVQs can be awarded, or elements of NVQs credited by APL.

*Gather the appropriate evidence. It will be in several forms eg certificates, references, details of previous employment.

*Submit this is an orderly form - the portfolio of evidence, and be prepared to be interviewed in depth by the assessor.

*Receive the decision of the assessor. This may be to make a full award, give credits for elements of the award or to state that the candidate has not yet proved her competence.

APL is not necessarily a short cut or a cheap route to gaining an NVQ because it involves considerable time and effort to put together a portfolio that will satisfy an assessor. But it does enable individuals to obtain recognition of personal competencies previously gained. Furthermore an individual need not necessarily by employed in the occupational area to gain an NVQ through Apl, though an assessor will not be satisfied unless the assessor is convinced that the candidate's competences are currently applicable to work. In other words the candidate must not be demonstrating outdated skills.

Who Can Be An Assessor?

The assessor is the key person in the process of assessing a candidates competencies. The assessor should be someone who has:

*Experience of the candidate's occupational area and who is knowledgeable and competent.

*Regular access to the candidate in all work situations.

*Been trained and registered as an assessor.

Not all employees, however experienced at work and desirous of becoming assessors they may be, are suited to be assessors, and since they play a crucial role they should be avoided. Assessors should be selected with great care. They must be capable of gaining the confidence of co-workers, helping them to prepare for their assessments and of giving reliable, objective and honest assessments.

Likewise there are experienced, knowledgeable care staff, with the potential to become excellent assessors, but who doubt their own abilities. These people need to be identified, encouraged to undergo training and supported by the manager. This support is essential because the role of assessor is quite different from that of a care worker and many newly qualified assessors are hesitant in the assessment process because of their lack of self confidence.

Who Else Is Involved In The Assessment Of Candidates?

*Advisor/Mentor - someone, other than the assessor, who has regular contact with the candidate at work and, familiar with NVQ assessment, is able to provide encouragement and support to the candidate. The advisor/mentor may be a line manager or close co-worker.

*Internal Verifier - this trained and registered person ensures that the assessments made by assessors within an organisation are both fair and standardised throughout that organisation. Internal verifiers may be employees of the organisation or representatives of the assessment centre.

*External Verifier - appointed by the awarding body to satisfy it that its awards are being properly made.External Verifiers will question internal verifiers on their work and sample the assessments or their assessors.

The Structure of NVQ Care Awards

As discussed previously NVQ awards will be available in most occupational areas and all will have the same framework and structure for recognising competence.

This framework has five levels which, for general guidance alone, are defined as follows:

Level 1: competence in the performance of work activities which are in the main routine and predictable or provide a broad foundation, primarily as a basis for progression.

Level 2: competence in a broader and more demanding range of work activities, involving greater individual responsibility and autonomy than at level 1.

Level 3: competence in skilled areas that involve performance of a broad range of work activities, including many that are complex and non-routine. In some areas, supervisory competence may be a requirement at this level.

Level 4: competence in the performance of complex, technical specialised and professional work activities, including those involving design, planning and problem-solving, with a significant degree of personal accountability. In many areas, supervisory competence in supervision or management will be a requirement at this level.

Level 5: competence which involves the application of a significant range of fundamental principals and complex techniques across a wide and often unpredictable variety of contexts. Personal accountability and autonomy feature strongly and often significant responsibility for the work of others and for the allocation of substantial resources.

Although care awards are currently only available at level 2 and level 3 this does not discount the possibility of other levels being developed in the future. The absence of level 1 will not disbar an individual from preparing for a level 2 award since individual should enter the NVQ system at the level most appropriate to their needs. In fact level 2 will be the most relevant entry point for many residential care workers.

Figure 6.1 shows the hierarchical structure of a NVQ award. Although it is easier to understand this structure by working down the hierarchy from the title and level, the philosophical structure of NVQs is the other way round. The award is built up from a foundation of work based competencies and cannot be achieved until the prescribed number of competencies have been properly proved.

Figure 6.1 Structure of an NVQ Award

STRUCTURE OF AN NVQ AWARD

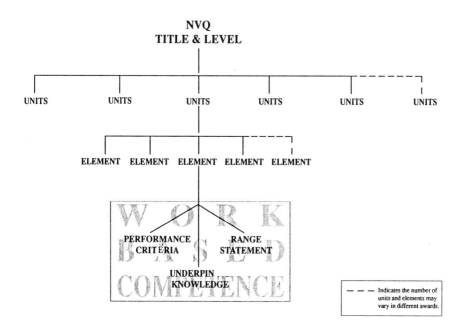

Each unit, in turn, is sub-divided into own prescribed and coded elements of competence.

An element, the smallest assessable part of an award, is defined as a competence, at the stated level, by three accompanying characteristics. These are:

Performance Criteria. These define the acceptable level of competence - normally as achievements but sometimes by the manner in which they are achieved. The definitions used must be unambiguous and written so that performance can be readily measured against them.

Range Statements. These define the circumstances under which the competence must be demonstrated. For example different clients, specified situations or using various aids.

Underpinning Knowledge. This outlines the degree of awareness the candidate must have of the relevant theory and principles that contribute to proper performance and which will enable the candidate to transfer the demonstrated competence to different work situations. Where this knowledge cannot be inferred by the assessor from the actions of the candidate, then the assessor must establish supporting evidence by questioning the candidate.

The Content of NVQ Level 2 in Care

There are currently six awards at this level. Each award is made up from a group of Core Units (which are common to each of the six awards) plus one of the groups of Endorsement Units. This is shown diagrammatically in Figure 6.2

The Care Sector Consortium under Crown Copyright (1992) has prepared detailed models of the core units at Levels 2 and 3. Included here is the Summary of Core and Endorsement Units for Level II in Care.

Core

O Overall principle: Promote equality for all individuals

Z1* Contribute to the protection of individuals from abuse

W2* Contribute to the ongoing support of clients and others significant to them

W3* Support clients in transition due to their care requirements

U4* Contribute to the health, safety and security of individuals & their environment.

NVQ LEVEL 2 AWARDS IN CARE

| CORE UNITS | + | ENDORSEMENT UNITS | = | NVQ AWARD |

CORE UNITS + DEVELOPMENT CARE UNITS = DEVELOPMENT CARE

+ DIRECT CARE UNITS = DIRECT CARE

+ DOMICILIARY SUPPORT UNITS = DOMICILIARY SUPPORT

+ RESIDENTIAL/ HOSPITAL SUPPORT UNITS = RESIDENTIAL/ HOSPITAL SUPPORT

+ POST NATAL CARE UNITS = POST NATAL CARE

+ SPECIAL CARE UNITS = SPECIAL CARE

+ OTHERS TO BE DEVELOPED

U5* Obtain, transmit and store information relating to the delivery of a care service

The above Core Units when supported by more detailed Endorsement Units of study will earn an NVQ award. The Units for Endorsement are in a series of six award subjects as listed, namely: Development Care, Direct Care, Domiciliary Support, Residential/Hospital Support, Post Natal Care, and Special Care, with others to be developed. Under each Endorsement Unit there is a series of modules to be carried out in the work-place. As a relevant example, the encoded modules of competency are listed here for Residential/hospital support:

Z7 Contribute to the movement & treatment of clients to maximise their physical comfort

Z10 Enable clients to eat and drink

Z11 Enable clients to access and use toilet facilities

U1 Contribute to the maintenance and management of domestic and personal resources

U2 Maintain and control stock, equipment & materials

Each of the six Units for Endorsement has equivalent areas for the learner to understand and to achieve skillfully with the client.

As with the level 2 awards those at level 3 have a group of Core Units, common to all awards at this level, which must be assessed in conjunction with one of the groups of Endorsement Units. Endorsement Unit groups are of two broad kinds, those concerned with care areas and those relating to specific need.

Level 3 Core Units

O Overall principle: Promote equality for all individuals

Z1* contribute to the protection of individuals from abuse

Z3* contribute to the management of aggressive & abusive behaviour

Z4* promote communication with clients where there are communication difficulties

Z8* support clients when they are distressed

Y2* enable clients to make use of available services & information

U4* contribute to the health, safety and security of individuals & their environment

U5* obtain, transmit and store information relating to the delivery of a care service

Each of these core units is developed within the endorsement units to earn the NVQ in Care. The endorsement units at Level III are greater in number: Promoting Independence, Supported Living, Rehabilitative Care, Continuing Care, Supportive Long-Term Care, Terminal Care, Acute Care, Acute Care (Children), Clinic and out-patient care, Substance Use, Support & Protection, Self and environmental management skills, Mental health care, Mobility & movement, with Communication, Foot care and others still in development stages.

As a relevant example the endorsement units for Supportive long-term care are listed below:

Z12 Contribute to the management of client continence

X10 Support professionals by assisting with and carrying out agreed physiotherapy movement programmes

X12 Support professionals with clinical activities

X13 Prepare and undertake agreed clinical activities with clients whose health is stable in non-acute care settings

V1 Contribute to the planning and monitoring of service delivery

U3 Prepare and maintain environments for clinical procedures

Which Units to Select for Staff?

Although a candidate can be assessed for individual units of competence, and be awarded credits (Record of Achievement), to obtain the full award they must be successfully assessed for all the Core Units and all the Endorsement Units with a named group. It may very well appear to a Manager that not all the units in a endorsement group seem to be the most relevant for the staff in the particular home and that she would prefer to select her own choice from the full list of units. Unfortunately at present this is not possible; if the staff are to obtain a NVQ award they must be assessed for all the prescribed units. If, as sometimes happens, it is not possible for staff to be assessed for a particular unit in the Home where they work then arrangements will have to be made for that assessment to take place elsewhere - which is often not as difficult as it may first seem.

Getting Started With NVQs

When the decision has been taken to become involved with NVQ awards the important first step is to explain to the care staff the reasons for the decision and the benefits to individuals and the Home. A few staff will already be aware of NVQs and be impatient for their implementation. Some will feel that training is of no use to them, have they not been doing the job for years (these are probably the ones most in need of training), whereas the majority will welcome the interest taken in them by management, but be apprehensive about what it involves. What will it require of them in terms of training, time and worry? This is why it is necessary for the Home Manager to be familiar with the structure of NVQs so that she can answer their questions, give reassurance and encouragement.

The next step is to become associated with an awarding body for the Integrated Care Awards. Large organisations, involving several residential homes backed by the resources of HQ staff, may decide to apply to become an assessment centre directly to one of the awarding bodies. In this case advice and support should be sought from the local TEC (Training and Enterprise Council) which, with the chosen awarding body, will assist with the process of becoming an approved assessment centre. Smaller homes are more likely to elect to become a member of local consortium or, if none already exist, to form one in association with other like-minded homes. If a home's manager is not aware of local consortia then she can find out about them through her local TEC. If none exist then she may wish to take the initiative by contacting managers of other homes in her area with the aim of creating their own consortium. Again TECs will be helpful with the process.

An alternative option, for large organisations or single homes, is to contact the principal of a college of further education with a request for assistance in delivering NVQ awards. Some colleges are already approved assessment centres for a range of NVQs and will be most willing to assist, however small or large the number of potential candidates may be. But time spent making enquiries about the services offered by various colleges will be well spent, as the services may vary considerably.

Local colleges are now independent corporations and many operate outside of their previous catchment areas, some providing services on a national level. Surprisingly the more progressive colleges may well be able to provide the necessary support for NVQ training at little or no cost to the home or organisation.

Although the Home's Manager may concentrate initial energies on implementing NVQ awards for the care staff, NVQ awards also exist for other occupational areas. The needs of domestic and catering staff should equally be considered, for they too make an essential contribution to the quality of care In a residential home.

Although it is usual for the employer to bear the cost of in-service training the government has demonstrated its commitment to NVQ training awards by allowing individuals who pay their own fees to claim tax relief on the amount paid.

6.5 General National Vocational Qualifications (GNVQs)

Although a Home's Manager will not normally be involved with GNVQs as part of in-service training strategy, she is increasingly likely to come in contact with them when considering applicants who have completed a vocational course at college. Because of their very close relationship to NVQs they are briefly discussed here, rather than in the section on recruitment.

In 1991 the NCVQ was instructed by the government to develop GNVQs to provide broad-cased vocational educational qualifications, for people not in employment, that would be equally valid routes into higher education or employment. (SCOTVEC was similarly required to produce General Scottish Vocational Qualifications - GSVQs.) GNVQs, which are usually prepared for through schools or colleges, concentrate more on the theoretical competences underpinning vocational skills, relevant to an occupational area, than the actual vocational competencies themselves. This is because it is only at work that vocational competencies can be assessed.

GNVQs mirror the structure of NVQs in that they have units and elements of competence with associated performance criteria and range statements. Five levels are planned but the first three are the ones the Home's Manager is most likely to come into contact with.

Foundation Level. An introductory level for those who need time (generally a year) and an interest in a vocational area to develop their educational skills before progressing to a higher GNVQ level or to employment and NVQ.

Intermediate Level. Broadly equivalent to GCSE study but with a strong vocational emphasis in an occupational area. Usually prepared for over one year. Students may progress to GNVQ advanced level or to employment and NVQ training.

Advanced Level. Broadly equivalent to two GCE advanced level passes, again with a strong vocational emphasis. Students may progress directly to employment and NVQ awards, or provided they have taken sufficient units, to a place in higher education.

The Care Sector Consortium has accredited BTEC, C&G and the CCETSW to validate assessment centres for the award of GNVQs in Health and Care.

GNVQs have now replaced most of the various certificates that were previously awarded by these bodies in this occupational area. In future there should be no reason for a Home Manager to be confused about the relative merits or standards of various certificates held by prospective employees. This was, of course, one of the government's reasons for establishing the NCVQ in the first place.

CHAPTER 7
The Registration & Inspection of Residential Care Homes

REGISTRATION OF HOMES

7.1 Introduction to The Act

The Registered Homes Act 1984, enacted in April 1985, requires

"Any establishment which provides or is intended to provide, whether for reward or not, residential accommodation with both board and personal care for persons in need of personal care by reason of old age, disablement, past or present dependence on alcohol or drugs, or past or present mental disorder..." to register under Part I of the Act as a residential care home.

Old age, disablement, alcohol/drug dependency and mental disorder are the four different categories of residents for which residential care homes can be registered.

The act exempts from the need to register several types of homes, the most notable of which are:

* Residential care homes accommodating fewer than four persons.

* Residential care homes owned and managed by a local authority.

* Any establishment constituted by an Act of Parliament, or incorporated by Royal Charter (eg Salvation Army).

The registration authority is the social services authority for the area in which the home is located.

The Act aims to safeguard the health and well-being of residents by:

* Ensuring the person (or persons) who owns and/or manages the home is a suitable person to run a residential home.

* Ensuring the situation of the building, its structure, accommodation, equipment and staffing are appropriate for a residential home.

* Ensuring that the aims and objectives of the home are such as to provide properly for the needs of the residents.

These criteria (as specified in Section 9 a, b and c of the Act) are the basis on which the registration authority must decide whether or not to register a particular home.

7.2 Registration Process

It is important to note that the registration of a home cannot be transferred from an existing owner to a new purchaser. The person acquiring a home must seek registration for himself, his manager if he is to employ one, the building and the Home's aims and objectives.

Therefore, since all intending purchasers of residential homes are entitled to one free ocnsultation with an inspector from the registration authority they are well-advised to contact the registration authority before making any commitment to buy. This advice applies equally to those seeking to purchase a building for later conversion to a residential home.

Prospective owners need to establish early in the proceedings:

* If there is any likely reason why they should not be registered as an owner.

* If the registration authority will require alterations to the fabric of an existing home before registering it with a new owner.

* In the case of a building to be converted to a residential home, if its situation is such that the registration authority would register it.

* If there is likely to be a continuing demand for such a home, or if an alternative category of resident would be more commercially viable.

The enthusiasm prospective owners may have to acquire residential homes should not blind them to the prudence of seeking early advice from registration authority inspectors. The advice received may well prevent them acting on assumptions, falsely based, that later prove to be extremely expensive. Most registration authorities help applicants with the process of registration by issuing a pre-registration information pack which, ideally, will contain:

*An Application for Registration Form

*A copy of the Registered Homes Act 1984 and the Residential Care Homes Regulations 1984.

*A copy of the registration authority's own requirements for registration.

*A copy of 'Home Life' -- the code of conduct for residential care.

*Guidance on preparing aims and objectives.

*Guidance on preparing a business plan.

*A checklist for the documents to be included with the application for registration.

If a pre-registration pack is not issued then those applying for registration should ask their registration authority's registration and inspection unit how they can obtain this essential information and guidance.

7.3 The persons who must be registered: Section 9a of the Act

a) The person, or persons, who will be in control of the Home. this may be the owner; the leaseholder; both partners of a partnership; or in the case of a company or voluntary organisation -- the manager or chairman and the company secretary.

b) The person who will manage the home, if this is not also the person in control of the Home.

Before any of the above individuals can be registered they must satisfy the registration authority that they are 'fit persons' under the Act. This will involve them in supplying the registration authority with:

*Details of their professional/technical qualifications and experience, if any, of running a residential care home.

*Names and addresses of previous employers.

*Names and addresses of two referees.

*Their consent to a police check to reveal details of any convictions they may have had.

*A report from a registered medical practitioner on the state of their health.

With regard to the person, or persons, who will be in control of the Home the registration authority will be looking for individuals of honesty and integrity, with the resources and business acumen to operate successfully a residential care home. A person in charge of a residential home need not have personal experience of residential care if the intention is to appoint a suitable qualified and experienced manager.

As a further precaution the registration authority will have the names of the people included in an application for registration checked against the Department of Health list of 'unfit persons'. This list includes the names of people who have previously applied for registration and been refused and those who have had their registration cancelled.

7.4 The building has to be registered -- Section 9b of the Act

In deciding whether or not the building intended to be used as a residential care home is suitable for registration, the registration authority will question:

* The location of the building, eg, Is it appropriate for elderly persons?

* The construction and state of the building, eg, Is it sound, well-maintained and safe for occupation by elderly persons?

* The accommodation provided within the building, eg, Does it meet the standards set in the registration authority's own requirements for registration?

* The proposed staffing levels, eg, Are these sufficient to meet the authority's own requirements for registration taking into account, amongst other considerations, the internal design of the building and the Home's aims and objectives?

* Equipment provided, eg, Will the aids, adaptations and fittings provided meet the needs of the category of residents for which registration is being sought?

The Residential Care Homes Regulations give guidance to registration authorities on the above, but since the words 'adequate' and 'reasonable' are frequently used much is left to the interpretation of individual authorities. It is for this reason that registration authorities have developed their own, more specific, guidelines and why it is important for those seeking registration to refer to these local guidelines, and to discuss matters and any potential problems, with a registration and inspection officer.

During the process of registration the officer involved will consult with the relevant Planning Department (planning permission is a pre-requisite for registration), the Building Control Department, the Fire Prevention Department and the Environmental Health Department. All these departments must be satisfied that the building is suitable for registration.

7.5 The aims and objectives must be registered -- Section 9c of the Act
(The way in which it is intended to carry on the work of the Home)

The registration authority will have to satisfy itself regarding the proposed AIMS, OBJECTIVES, POLICY & PROCEDURES of the Home.

The authority will look in detail at:

* Stated Aims and Objectives. Are these appropriate to the health and well-being of the prospective residents?

* Business Plan. Does this project financial viability for the Home to safeguard the security of residents?

* Staff job descriptions and contracts of employment. Do these meet the minimum legal requirements?

* Residents' contracts. Do these state the fee to be paid and the services to be provided for the fee?

* Proposed methods of maintaining records. Will these satisfy requirements in Schedule 2 of the Residential Care Homes Regulations, 1984?

The time involved in registering a Home from initial enquiries, through receipt of application forms, to the issue of the registration certificate will vary considerably depending upon individual circumstances associated with the people to be registered, the building and the way it is intended the Home will be run. The average time is approximately three months, though this is only to indicate that it may be less and possibly longer.

The registration authority will charge a fee, which is fixed nationally, for processing registration. This is currently 840 pounds plus a further 230 pounds if a Manager is also to be registered. When registration is granted the registration authority will issue a Registration Certificate, stating:

* The name/s of the Owner and Manager.

* The number of persons for whom residential accommodation can be provided at any one time.

* The age and category of residents to be accommodated.

This certificate must be displayed, in a prominent position, within the Home.

In addition to the initial registration fee an annual fee will be charged by the registration authority. This will be based on the number of residents the Home is registered to accommodate. It will be payable one month after registration and on the anniversary of this date thereafter.

7.6 Procedure for appeal against refusal to grant registration

A registration authority is required to grant registration of a Home unless it can demonstrate conclusively that the requirements of Sections 9a, b and c of the Act have not been met. If an authority believes that these requirements have not been met then it will issue a Notice of Proposal to Refuse Registration. Such a notice will state the authority's reasons for the proposed refusal. On receipt of such a notice the applicant has 14 days in which to require the authority to give him an opportunity to appeal to it concerning the proposed refusal.

The applicant may submit his appeal either orally or in writing and this will be considered by a sub-committee of counsellors of the registration authority established for the purpose of hearing appeals. In hearing the appeal the committee members will listen to the evidence presented by the registration and inspection officer and consider the submissions put by the applicant. The members will then decide either to accept the proposal to refuse registration, or to reject the proposed refusal to grant registration. An appeal against the decision of such a committee not to grant registration must be made within 28 days to the Registered Homes Tribunal. Details of how to appeal will accompany any refusal to grant registration.

The Registered Homes Tribunal will consider each case on its merits. It may decide to agree with the original refusal or to set aside, or otherwise vary, the registration authority's own guidelines that led to the refusal to grant registration. It is not necessary for appellants to the Tribunals to be legally represented, but since they will have already invested considerable time and money in reaching this stage, they are well advised to be properly represented.

INSPECTION OF HOMES

7.7 Basis for Inspections

The Residential Care Homes Regulations, 1984, as subsequently amended in minor detail by Local Authority Circulars from the Department of Health, amongst other things prescribe for the conduct of Homes; the provision of facilities and services; and the records that must be maintained.

It is against the background of these Regulations that inspection officers of the registration authority will inspect a registered home. The inspectors will also refer to *Home Life,* the recognised code of practise for residential care. Although this latter publication has no legal standing it is widely referred to by registration authorities and Registered Homes Tribunals. There is no point in reproducing here extracts or summaries of these two publications as they are documents which all Home Managers should keep close at hand and refer to regularly.

Homes Are For Living In is a third publication that Managers should read on a regular basis. Published by the HMSO for the Department of Health Social Services Inspectorate, it offers a model for evaluating quality of care provided, and quality of life experienced, in residential care homes for elderly people. In this book the factors which contribute to good quality care and good life experience within Homes are identified and grouped around six basic values:

* Privacy

* Dignity

* Independence

* Choice

* Rights

* Fulfilment

Each value is precisely defined by statements about how a Home should be organised and what it should be doing to promote these values in the interests of residents.

These values, and their accompanying statements, are arranged in the form of checklists. They are commonly used as the criteria against which professional judgements about the actual standards of care practice in a Home can be made. This valuable document is not only an *aide memoire* for inspectors, but also useful for Home Managers to monitor the quality of provision they are making in their Homes.

7.8 Inspections & their conduct

The registration authority may inspect a registered home on such occasions, and at such intervals, as it may decide, but it must do so not less than twice in every 12 month period. It is an offence against the Registered Homes Act 1984 to refuse admission to a duly authorised person, at anytime, for the purpose of inspecting a registered home, or any establishment which that person reasonably suspects is being used as a residential home. It is also an offence not to make available for inspection, at all times, the records the Home is required to keep, or to refuse facilities for an inspector to speak privately with a resident.

If the registration authority, through want of resources or by policy, only inspects its Home twice yearly, then it is likely to do so on the basis of one inspection for which prior notice has been given and one completely unannounced inspection. For announced inspections the Manager, and usually the proprietor (if not the manager), will be expected to be present.

The purpose of any inspection is to determine whether or not a Home is complying with the terms and conditions of its registration and conducting itself in accordance with both the Residential Care Homes Regulations and the registration authority's own local requirements. But the depth of an inspection will depend upon several factors including the frequency of inspections, the resources of the inspection team and any concerns the inspectors may have about a particular home. Inspections may therefore last for anything from part of a day to a whole week.

Similarly the format of inspections will vary. Inspectors may choose to range over all the regulations pertaining to the running of a Home by inspecting samples of a Home's records, its staff rotas, menus, accommodation, kitchen facilities and fire precautions for example, as well as interviewing some residents and staff, either singly or in groups.

Alternatively, depending upon the registration authority's policy, the inspectors may elect to concentrate on just one of the six basic values identified in *Homes Are For Living In* and carry out an in-depth inspection on, say, privacy and determine to what extent the Home is meeting the needs of residents regarding this value.

7.8 Relationships with Inspectors

It is understandable that Home Managers do not like being inspected since a possible outcome of an inspection is that their professional achievements may be questioned. Furthermore, Home Managers can be held personally responsible for their actions. In extreme cases they may even be prosecuted and, if found guilty, have their names entered on the list of 'unfit persons' who may not be registered to run a residential home in the future.

It is not surprising therefore that inspections can be stressful occasions for managers and that their mounting tensions may be communicated to staff and residents, to everyone's detriment. Inspectors, too, are human. They function under their own pressures; they have inspection targets to reach, reports to compile, distressing complaints to investigate. They work in the knowledge that they too will be held accountable if they fail to recognise real or potential situations in their Homes that later are the cause of serious incidents. Inspectors also share with Home Managers and employees everywhere, the extreme difficulty in divorcing completely their non-working life from their professional functions. We all have our good and bad days, no matter how hard we try to be otherwise.

Given this, it is essential that a Home Manager adopts a successful strategy to cope with inspections that will minimise stress and gain from an inspection the maximum of benefit. Inspections are meant to lead to an improvement in care, which should be an objective mutually shared.

If a Home Manager is genuinely concerned about the health, well-being and fulfilment of her residents then from the onset she should resolve to see her inspector as a valuable and supportive ally, not as a hostile intruder who she has to deceive or placate to survive. Being uncooperative, trying to hide difficulties, warning staff and residents to be on their guard -- 'the inspector is coming', serves only to heighten tensions within the Home and to arouse the suspicions of an experienced inspector.

In the course of their work inspectors visit many Homes, and see examples of good and poor practice, ideas that work and those that do not. They are aware of local demographic trends, services that are likely to be sought by future residents, categories of Homes that are likely to succeed and those less likely. They are in the position to advise, guide and support a Home Manager, if she is wise enough to cultivate a proper professional relationship.

Furthermore inspectors are not blind to the commercial demands in the private sector, nor should they be. Businesses that fail often create innumerable hardships for the residents involved, for whom the inspector has a shared responsibility, and add to an inspector's worry and work load. Neither are inspectors unaware of the fact that a Home Manager may have two masters to serve, one being the Registered Homes Act with its associated regulations and the other the Home owner. Should conflict arise between these two then the Manager may find strength in the support of the inspector.

An obvious coping strategy for a Home Manager to adopt is one of open, honest, cooperation between herself and the inspector that engenders a spirit of mutual respect. But having a strategy is one thing, putting it into effect is another. A strategy, that depends on developing a relationship of mutual trust and respect is not one that lends itself to being turned on and off to meet the convenience of the moment. A Manager who deploys this strategy cannot expect to gain the trust of the inspector if at the times of inspections she appears welcoming and cooperative, but at others is silent and secretive.

No Manager, however competent and well-served by able staff she may be, can hope to get everything right all the time. People, whether they are staff, residents or relatives, are difficult to manage. Things do go wrong --accidents can happen, staff may cause problems, occupancy levels will fall and relatives and residents do complain, rightly or wrongly.

When incidents occur, other than of a routine nature, the Manager should take the initiative and contact the inspector rather than gamble on the possibility that events will go unnoticed. Such matters have the habit of coming to the attention of inspectors and the Manager then is placed on the defensive. Far better it is to speak to the inspector from the start, explain the situation, seek advice and discuss the possible remedies. Inspectors can, and do, apply for variations of local authority regulations when they think it is appropriate in the circumstances. Taking the initiative and making the first contact may appear to require courage but it is a policy that will do much to cement the desire working relationship.

Similarly when an inspection reveals some deficiency the sensible Manager rejects the impulse to be obstructive and defensive. She acknowledges the facts, listens to advice and exchanges ideas and possible solutions. Then of her own volition informs the inspector of the progress that she is making, or the difficulties she is still facing, rather than waiting for the inspector to make the necessary follow-up checks.

On completion of an inspection a detailed report will be prepared. This should indicate the strengths as well as any weaknesses in the Home that may have been revealed by the inspection. These inspection reports are then made available for the public, but equally important to the Manager is the fact that service purchasers will also read the reports. The content of reports is therefore of no mean importance to those concerned with the commercial success of a Home.

It is recommended practice that the inspector shows the Home Manager a draft of the report before it is published. This gives the Mdanager an opportunity to discuss the report with her inspector and, if possible, agree its content and emphasis. Any matters of possible dispute in a report are far more likely to be reconciled when each trusts to the professional integrity of the other.

7.9 Power to Enforce Regulations

Where the registration authority considers that a person registered under the Act has contravened or failed to comply with one or more of the regulations 6,10,11,13,14,15,16 or 19 of the Residential Care Homes Regulations, a notice may be served on the registered person. This will specify:

a) How the person has failed or is failing to comply with a regulation.

b) What action must be taken to comply.

c) The period, not being less than 3 months, within which the person registered must take action to comply.

No offence under the Registered Homes Act will actually have been committed until the period of time specified in the notice has expired. If after the expiry date the person registered has not taken action to the satisfaction of the authority then a summons for the registered person to appear in court will be issued. If the magistrates reject the defence and find the person guilty of an offence under the Act they will impose a fine.

Failure to comply with the regulation after being found guilty may result in another summons being issued and a further appearance in court. Alternatively if the failure to comply is considered by the registration authority to be sufficiently serious it may issue a notice of cancellation of registration under Section 10 of the Registered Homes Act 1984.

REFERENCES AND FURTHER READING

Blake R R and Mouton J S, **The Managerial Grid,** Gulf Publishing, Houston, Texas 1964. The Managerial Grid figure from **The New Managerial Grid,** by Robert R Blake and Jane Stygley Mouton. Houston: Gulf Publishing Company, (1978).

Blake R R and Mouton J S, (1981) **Towards Resolution of the Situationalism vs 'One Best Style . . . '** Scientific Methods Inc, Austin, Texas.

Brown J A C, **The Social Psychology of Industry, (1954)** pp 219-226. Pelican Books.

Brown M and Henderson J, 'Organisation of Work - Two Approaches', in **Industrial Society** (October 1968).

Herzberg F, **Work and the Nature of Man.** Granada Publishing Ltd, St Albans (1968).

Herzberg F, Mausner B, and Sneiderman B B, **The Motivation to Work,** 2nd ed, Wiley (1959).

Maslow A H, **Motivation and Personality,** 2nd ed, Harper and Row (1954).

McGregor D M. 'The Human Side of Enterprise' in **Adventure in Thought and Action,** McGraw Hill, New York 1960. Proceedings of the fifth anniversary convocation of the MIT School of Industrial Management (1957).

Morris D, **Manwatching.** A field guide to human behaviour. Triad/Panther (1978).

National Council of Social Service. **Caring for People: Staffing Residential Homes,** Report of the Committee of Enquiry. Chairman, Professor Lady Williams, George Allen & Unwin Ltd, (1967).

References & Further Reading -- Third Edition, 1996

Centre for Policy on Ageing, **Home Life**

Fletcher, S, **NVQs Standards and Competence,** Kogan Page.

HMSO, **National Occupational Standards for Care** (Care Sector Consortium)

    Homes Are For Living In

    Registered Homes Act 1984

    The Residential Care Homes Regulations 1984

Meteyard, B., **Getting Started with NVQ,** Longman

Whitear, G., **The NVQ Handbook,** Pitman